MENTAL HEALTH VOLUNTEERS

MENTAL HEALTH VOLUNTEERS

The Expanding Role of the Volunteer in Hospital and Community Mental Health Services

Edited by

PATRICIA L. EWALT

Demonstration Officer
Massachusetts Mental Health Center
Boston, Massachusetts

With a Foreword by

MILTON GREENBLATT, M.D.

Professor of Psychiatry
Tufts University School of Medicine
Superintendent, Boston State Hospital
Boston, Massachusetts

Proceedings of a Conference
Sponsored by
THE MASSACHUSETTS ASSOCIATION FOR MENTAL HEALTH

CHARLES C THOMAS • PUBLISHER
Springfield • Illinois • U.S.A.

Published and Distributed Throughout the World by
CHARLES C THOMAS • PUBLISHER
BANNERSTONE HOUSE
301-327 East Lawrence Avenue, Springfield, Illinois, U.S.A.
NATCHEZ PLANTATION HOUSE
735 North Atlantic Boulevard, Fort Lauderdale, Florida, U.S.A.

*With THOMAS BOOKS careful attention is given to all details of
manufacturing and design. It is the Publisher's desire to present books
that are satisfactory as to their physical qualities and artistic possibilities
and appropriate for their particular use. THOMAS BOOKS will be true
to those laws of quality that assure a good name and good will.*

Printed in the United States of America
A-2

v

CONTRIBUTORS

LIBBIE B. BOWER, Ph.D.
Consultant
Massachusetts Association for Mental Health, Inc.
Boston, Massachusetts

EILEEN CORNING
Rehabilitation Committee
Mental Health Association of the North Shore
Salem, Massachusetts

MARY DAVIS
Chairman, Volunteer Committee
Massachusetts Association for Mental Health, Inc.
Norfolk Mental Health Association, Inc.
Norwood, Massachusetts

PRESTON DAVIS, Ph.D.
Chief Psychologist
Medfield State Hospital
Harding, Massachusetts

DORIS WRIGHT EPSTEIN, M.S.W.
Supervisor
Mental Health Case Aide Program at the Metropolitan State Hospital
Mystic Valley Mental Health Association
Lexington, Massachusetts

PATRICIA L. EWALT
Demonstration Officer
Massachusetts Mental Health Center
Boston, Massachusetts

VICTOR A. GELINEAU, Ph.D.
Consultant Coordinator, Case Aide Program
Boston State Hospital
Boston, Massachusetts

REBECCA GLASMANN, A.C.S.W.
Chief, Social Work Service
Veterans Administration Hospital
Bedford, Massachusetts

MILTON GREENBLATT, M.D.
Professor of Psychiatry
Tufts University School of Medicine
Superintendent
Boston State Hospital
Boston, Massachusetts

SAMUEL GROB, Ph.D.
Executive Director
Center House Foundation
Center Club
Boston, Massachusetts

ROBERT C. HUNT, M.D.
State of New York
Department of Mental Hygiene
Albany, New York

DAVID KANTOR, Ph.D.
Special Fellow, National Institute of Mental Health
Boston State Hospital
Boston, Massachusetts

ELIZABETH HODGMAN, A.C.S.W.
Psychiatric Social Worker
Brookline Mental Health Clinic
Brookline, Massachusetts

ERNEST KRAUS, M.S.W.
Formerly, VISTA Coordinator
Boston State Hospital
Boston, Massachusetts

DAVID O. McGAVERN, M.S.W.
Formerly, Director of Selection
Commonwealth Service Corps
Boston, Massachusetts

WILLIAM NETH
Community Coordinator
Massachusetts Commission for the Aging
Boston, Massachusetts

HELEN REINHERZ, Sc.D.
Associate Professor
Simmons College School of Social Work
Boston, Massachusetts

ELIZABETH MARY REMAR
Director of Volunteer Services
Boston State Hospital
Boston, Massachusetts

IRVING SANDERS, M.A.

Executive Director
Norfolk Mental Health Association, Inc.
Norwood, Massachusetts

EDNA STEIN

President
Brookline Association for Mental Health
Brookline, Massachuetts

NICHOLAS THISSE, Ed.M.

Coordinator
Patients Rehabilitation Occupational Program, Inc.
Boston State Hospital
Boston, Massachusetts

RUTH TURNER

Assistant Director, Volunteer Services
Veterans Administration Hospital
Bedford, Massachusetts

ANNE UMANA VARGUS, A.C.S.W.

Chief of Volunteer Services
Greater Lawrence Guidance Center
Lawrence, Massachusetts

HAROLD M. VISOTSKY, M.D.

Director
State of Illinois Department of Mental Health
Chicago, Illinois

FOREWORD

VOLUNTEERISM HAS BEEN changing over the past decades as rapidly as psychiatry itself. Not many years ago it was essentially limited to a few dedicated citizens, the "Lady Bountifuls," who left gifts for patients and made donations; or the enlightened community organization that ran a Christmas party or promoted a ballgame. Distance was the keynote and fear of the mentally ill its counterpart. Now, although these desirable charitable functions have not abated, we see on all sides an effort of citizens to work more closely with the caretaking staff, entering into much closer individual relationships with the mentally sick.

An historic milestone was the development of the student volunteer program for services to the mentally ill, beginning with Harvard and Radcliffe students in 1954. The movement was broadly based in the student body, was legitimated by prevailing student organizations and by the faculty, and concentrated its efforts upon the severely mentally ill. Although fear of psychological deviance was still there, it was overcome by the surge of undergraduate enthusiasm to right wrongs and to rescue the downtrodden from the results of neglect and dehumanization perpetrated by the older generation.

At any rate, college students popularized the challenge of working with the chronically ill, working with them not only in groups but individually in "case aide" arrangements and other personal relationships. They evolved innovations in rehabilitation such as the student-patient cooperative halfway house (Wellmet); developed conceptual frameworks for their so-called "friendship therapy"; and finally, proved that student attention could make patients well, even where long hospitalization and failure of previous staff efforts had sometimes labelled them as "hopeless."

Thus we see that the occasional generous-hearted "Lady Bountiful" who kept her distance was joined or even replaced by fiery young undergraduates who wanted to plunge in and live the lives of the underprivileged, the chronic rejects of society. They started a minor revolution by voicing a challenge and rallying call for the youth of the nation in colleges. They carried with them a conviction of the social nature of psychological maladaptation: the necessity to revamp not only the social structure of the hospital but also the underlying fabric of society and its attitude toward its deviants. They showed, too, the potency of sub-professionals as therapeutic agents, especially when properly inspired as they were. They embodied within their movement all the best conceptions of social psychiatry-in-action that characterized psychiatry's developments in the middle of the twentieth century.

The college undergraduates along with more adult volunteers (and soon a new element, the high school volunteer) showed that they could work effectively in at least three contexts: (1) within the hospital on the wards, as recreational aides, occupational aides, case aides and rehabilitation aides; (2) in transitional facilities such as day hospital, night hospital, halfway house, etc.; (3) in the community helping the resettlement of patients at home, in foster family placements, in nursing homes, apartment dwellings, and in the more elaborate process of realigning former patients with church, social and recreational organizations, educational facilities, and job opportunities.

Volunteering had now fully embarked upon its career in community psychiatry, that broad frontier that only the future can fully reveal to us. The variety of useful roles that volunteers can and will play, however, is partially defined by the chapters in this volume that deal with the volunteer in the community, by such interesting formulations as the "social aide" who works, as a specialty, with former patients in the community.

Volunteers have pointed out many directions in which citizens can help the mentally ill by assisting organizations devoted to promotion of mental health, but citizen participation has not stopped at this. Recently, especially with impetus of the poverty program and the encouragement of greater citizen involvement in mental health programs, citizen volunteers have sought to establish mental health facilities in the community dominated more or less by the community organization. While collaborating with professional staff and institutions, these facilities are not dependent altogether on professional sanction.

Local mental health organizations, for example, are seeking ways to come into their own. In some instances, they provide the essential ideas and funds for mental health programs, hiring professional staff to serve their clients and their purposes. These programs are not subordinate to mental hospitals, where the professional hierarchy is dominant. There is, after all, no limit imposed upon the conscience of the American who wants to help his fellow man, and it is obvious that to this point governmental and professional arrangements have left something to be desired in service to the multitude of the emotionally disturbed.

How this latter-day approach to volunteer activities in the community mental health period will work out is anybody's guess. However, some substantial and successful models recorded in this book give rise to the hope that intelligent three-way collaboration between the volunteer, the professional and the state representation is not only possible, but also that it may hold the key to highly desirable new dimensions of patient care. It behooves all of us to study these programs with an open mind, while we search within ourselves for those prejudices and barriers to clear thinking that might prevent the realization of valuable effort.

In this spirit we commend this interesting volume to the reader's study.

MILTON GREENBLATT, M.D.
Professor of Psychiatry
Tufts University School of Medicine
Superintendent, Boston State Hospital
Boston, Massachusetts

INTRODUCTION

IMPETUS FOR THE Massachusetts Association for Mental Health state-wide conference arose from recognition that care of the mentally ill is rapidly changing. With development of community mental health programs, there is opportunity to utilize fully the special capacities of volunteers.

Shorter periods of hospitalization and the necessity for more effective use of community resources, increased range of potential services, and manpower needs have all posed a challenge to mental health agencies.

This challenge stimulated the Massachusetts Association for Mental Health Volunteer Committee to provide new approaches in leadership for hundreds of volunteers working in our state's hospitals, clinics and communities.

The committee conducted a country-wide survey of volunteer activities and service programs. It was impressed with the range of new and promising demonstrations undertaken by many state divisions of our National Association for Mental Health.

Aware of comparable developments in Massachusetts, the committee concluded that a conference for volunteers and professional staff to discuss our state's ongoing programs would form an important first step in greater local implementation. Accordingly, a state-wide volunteer conference was scheduled at Boston State Hospital on October 27, 1965. The committee recommended publication of the conference proceedings as guidelines for community volunteers and hospital staff.

The goals of the conference were:

(1) To provide a setting in which volunteers and professional people could discuss problems to be resolved if more effective services are to be provided for the mentally ill. This discussion need not be negative since problems and issues can be the abrasive elements to sharpen understanding and effect positive action;

(2) To extend understanding of methods for volunteers and professional people to coordinate their efforts;

(3) To demonstrate a selected number of innovations which had been tested out in hospitals, clinics and the community in order to stimulate a high level of interest and strengthen local initiative.

Three nationally known keynote speakers prepared their presentations in harmony with the goals of the conference. Preconference working papers on each of the demonstrations were mailed to invitees. Each was requested to select the demonstration of his choice for a workshop assignment. Each workshop was assigned a team of professional and lay resource people who had developed demonstrations in their own settings.

Two hundred and fifty people attended, 60 per cent volunteers and 40 per cent professional persons. From the discussions, one could observe that new ideas were received, welcomed and evaluated by open minds; that the workshop discussions had special value because of personal involvement; that the volunteers and professional workers saw themselves as parts of a whole, not working in isolation with artificially determined boundary lines; that new programs can be developed cooperatively by knowledgeable men and women of integrity and goodwill. It was a growth experience.

A final plenary session reinforced the concept of the interdependence of professional workers and the volunteer. The challenges and opportunities were there to be seized if comprehensive community mental health services are to become a reality.

LIBBIE B. BOWER, PH.D.
Consultant
Massachusetts Association for
Mental Health

ACKNOWLEDGMENTS

SPACE DOES NOT permit individual mention of the large number of people who worked on the conference planning committee: the consultants, those who prepared the preconference working papers, and the tireless workers who carried out the myriad of details. A warm thanks is extended to all.

Special acknowledgment is due Mr. John McDade, Public Relations Director, Massachusetts Department of Mental Health, who worked with the planning committee over a long period of time and was largely responsible for the attendance of hospital administrators and other professional staff, as well as hospital volunteer directors. He observed that "such a conference would work toward welding together the community and the state hospital; the volunteer, because of her experience, could develop a far more receptive and supportive attitude on the part of other citizens toward the hospitalized patient; the potential for creative activities to meet gaps in service is enormous."

Doctor David Kantor, Special Fellow of the National Institute of Mental Health at Boston State Hospital, gave most generously of his time and skill, shared his experience, knowledge and research on volunteerism which provided a lever for the quality of the program.

Doctor Milton Greenblatt, Superintendent of Boston State Hospital and Professor of Psychiatry, Tufts University School of Medicine, despite the great demands on his time and energy, was continuously available to the chairman and her committee as a sounding board for ideas. He gave leadership in securing nationally known speakers, suggestions for the funding of the conference and publishing of the proceedings. He helped move the program from the planning to the action stage.

His staff, too, merits special mention, especially Mrs. Elizabeth Mary Remar, Director of Volunteer Services, and Mr. Ernest Kraus, Coordinator of VISTA Volunteers. Their work insured smooth functioning of the conference day . . . no easy task when meeting rooms were at a premium, schedules had to be shifted and other accommodations made with the least possible disruption to the hospital community.

Acknowledgment is gratefully made to Mrs. Robert W. Davis, Chairman, MAMH Volunteer Committee. She gave unstintingly to all phases of the conference planning. Her enthusiasm and capacity to work with a wide range of people in the community and hospital, both lay and professional, exemplified the purpose of the conference: the volunteer as a member of the therapeutic team.

Continued appreciation is expressed to Doctor Harry C. Solomon, Commissioner, Massachusetts Department of Mental Health, and Doctor Jack R. Ewalt, Director, Massachusetts Mental Health Center, and former Director, *Joint Commission on Mental Illness and Health,* two distinguished leaders whose work spearheaded the concept of the comprehensive community mental health programs in which the volunteer can make such a unique contribution.

Acknowledgment is made to the editors of *Bedford Research* for permission to republish the article, "Hidden Assets: A Youth Volunteer Program in a Psychiatric Hospital," which originally appeared in that journal, Volume 9, Number 2, Summer, 1963.

For the very considerable work in designing the format of the book, drawing up the guidelines for the chapters on the workshops, contacting the authors, deliberating with the editorial committee, and overseeing the preparation of the manuscript, the volunteer committee is deeply grateful to Mrs. Jack Ewalt.

The volunteeer committee further acknowledges the generosity of Roche Laboratories, Pfizer Laboratories, and Lakeside Laboratories, without whose financial contribution there would not have been a state-wide conference.

The Massachusetts Association for Mental Health is deeply grateful to Charles C Thomas, Publisher for the publication of the proceedings.

L.B.B.

CONFERENCE PLANNING COMMITTEE

Mrs. Robert Davis, Chairman
Mrs. James Adams
Mrs. Fred Blizard
Mrs. Reid Corning
Mr. Belden Daniels
Tobias Friedman, M.D.
Mrs. Lewis F. Good, Jr.
Milton Greenblatt, M.D.
Mrs. Leston Havens
Mrs. Kenneth Huberman

David Kantor, Ph.D.
Robert McCreech, M.A.
Mr. John McDade
Mrs. Hardwick Moseley
Mrs. Elizabeth Mary Remar
Mrs. Edward Rolfe
Mrs. Maida Solomon, M.S.W.
Mrs. Edna Stein
Mrs. Erik Stomstead
Mrs. James Williams

FACULTY OF THE CONFERENCE

Workshop Group Leaders

William Barnum, M.D.
J. Sanbourne Bockoven, M.D.
Jacob Christ, M.D.
Doris Fraser, M.S.S.S.
Victor Gelineau, Ph.D.
Robert Hunt, M.D.
Robert Hyde, M.D.
Peter Jenney, M.D.

Robert McCreech, M.A.
Mr. John McDade
Mark McGrath, M.S.W.
David Moriarty, M.D.
Kingman Price, M.D.
Phyllis Rolfe, M.S.S., Sc.M.
    Hyg.
Stephen Washburn, M.D.

Workshop Resource People

Mrs. Reid Corning
Mrs. Maurice Crevoshay
Mrs. Robert Davis
Mrs. Doris Epstein, M.S.W.
Mrs. Ann Evans, M.S.W.
Mrs. Esther Greenfield
Samuel Grob, Ph.D.

Mr. Jerry Hearsum
Mrs. Henry Hilliard
Elizabeth Hodgman, M.S.W.
Mrs. Rose Koltz
Ernest Kraus, M.S.W.
Mrs. Sidney Levin
Mr. John Levis

Mr. Matthew Luzzi
Robert McCreech, M.A.
David McGavern, M.S.W.
Mrs. Alfreda Peterson
Mrs. Elizabeth Mary Remar
Mrs. Edward Rolfe
Mrs. Theodore Russem
Mr. Theodore Schoenfeld

Willis C. Scott, M.S.W.
Mrs. Elayne Shulman
Mrs. Maida Solomon, M.S.W.
Mrs. Edna Stein
Nicholas Thisse, Ed.M.
Mrs. Barbara Valliere
Mrs. Anne Umana Vargus,
    M.S.S.S.

Recorders

Mrs. Margaret Dunn, M.S.W.
Mrs. Lewis F. Good, Jr.
Mrs. Leston Havens
Herbert Hoffman, Ph.D.
Mrs. Leila Keily
Mrs. Roberta Manton
Mr. Mark Mazel, M.S.S.S.

Mrs. Lucille McMahon
Mrs. H. Kelsea Moore
Mrs. Bernard Philips
Mrs. Rex Roberts
Mr. Irving Sanders, M.A.
Mrs. Thomas Wright

CONTENTS

                                                              Page
CONTRIBUTORS vii
FOREWORD—*Milton Greenblatt* xi
INTRODUCTION—*Libbie B. Bower* xv
ACKNOWLEDGMENTS xvii
CONFERENCE PLANNING COMMITTEE xix

PART I

Volunteers and Community Mental Health Services

Chapter
1. RETURNING THE VOLUNTEER TO THE COMMUNITY—
   Harold M. Visotsky 5
2. THE DEVELOPMENT OF A VOLUNTEER PROGRAM IN A
   COMMUNITY MENTAL HEALTH CLINIC—
   Anne Umana Vargus 12
3. THE COMMONWEALTH SERVICE CORPS: A DOMESTIC
   PEACE CORPS FOR MASSACHUSETTS—*David O. McGavern* 18

PART II

Developing Programs for Long-hospitalized Persons

4. THE CHANGING STATE HOSPITAL: WHAT IT NEEDS
   FROM VOLUNTEERS—*Robert C. Hunt* 25
5. COORDINATION OF VOLUNTEER SERVICES WITH OTHER
   DEPARTMENTS IN A MENTAL HOSPITAL—*William E. Neth* . . . 32
6. EXPLORATIONS OF THE VOLUNTEER ROLE: THE CASE
   AIDE PROGRAM AT BOSTON STATE HOSPITAL—
   Victor A. Gelineau 35
7. A MENTAL HEALTH ASSOCIATION CASE AIDE PROGRAM
   AT A LARGE STATE HOSPITAL—*Doris Wright Epstein* 45

Chapter　　　　　　　　　　　　　　　　　　　　　　　　　*Page*

8. THE VISTA VOLUNTEER PROGRAM AT THE BOSTON STATE
HOSPITAL—*Ernest A. Kraus* 52

9. "FASHION THERAPY": DIARY OF A REHABILITATION
TECHNIQUE FOR CHRONIC FEMALE PATIENTS—
Elizabeth Mary Remar 60

10. A MENTAL HEALTH ASSOCIATION PAID EMPLOYMENT
WORKSHOP IN A STATE HOSPITAL—*Edna Stein* 65

11. PROP: A SHELTERED WORKSHOP PROGRAM SPONSORED
BY VOLUNTEERS—*Nicholas H. Thisse* 73

PART III

Community Programs for Former Patients

12. THE COOPERATIVE APARTMENT: A MENTAL-HEALTH-
ASSOCIATION-SPONSORED RESIDENCE FOR RETURNING
PATIENTS—*Edna Stein* and *Elizabeth Hodgman* 79

13. THE ROLL OF VOLUNTEERS IN CENTER CLUB—*Samuel Grob* 89

14. THE TORCHLIGHTERS CLUB—*Eileen Corning* 95

15. THE CONCEPT OF A SOCIAL AIDE ORGANIZATION—..........
Mary Davis 99

16. CONTINUITY OF CARE IN VOLUNTEER SERVICES—
Irving Sanders 104

PART IV

Students in Mental Health Work

17. PROFESSIONAL SUPERVISION AS A MEANS OF ACHIEVING
VOLUNTEER PROGRAM GOALS—*Helen Reinherz* 111

18. HIDDEN ASSETS: A YOUTH VOLUNTEER PROGRAM IN A
PSYCHIATRIC HOSPITAL—*Rebecca Glasmann* and *Ruth Turner* 120

19. RECRUITING FOR MENTAL HEALTH WORK: REPORT OF A
PROGRAM WITH HIGH SCHOOL STUDENTS—
Patricia L. Ewalt and *Libbie B. Bower* 129

20. THE HUMAN RELATIONS LABORATORY: A COLLEGE
MENTAL HEALTH CAREERS PROGRAM—*Irving Sanders*
and *Preston Davis* 138

PART V

Volunteerism and Problems of Domain in the American Mental Health Movement

Chapter *Page*
21. VOLUNTEERISM AND PROBLEMS OF DOMAIN IN THE
    AMERICAN MENTAL HEALTH MOVEMENT—*David Kantor* 147

Index 157

MENTAL HEALTH VOLUNTEERS

Part 1
VOLUNTEERS AND COMMUNITY MENTAL HEALTH SERVICES

Chapter 1

RETURNING THE VOLUNTEER
TO THE COMMUNITY

HAROLD M. VISOTSKY, M.D.*

T HE FOCUS ON volunteers in the community has great significance
for volunteer activities in states throughout the nation. How well
volunteer programs succeed in the community will be an accurate
gauge of success of community-based mental health programs.

The shift from isolated and custodial state hospitals to community centers and general hospitals has been a major change in
mental health care. Day hospitals, night hospitals, weekend hospitals, halfway houses: all are comparatively new concepts for us
here in America.

Historically, the concept of volunteering has changed as well. It
began with a perfunctory acknowledgement of responsibility, perhaps in the form of a monetary donation. The next phase might
be called the coffee and cookies stage. This stage was guided by
a charitable instinct that was not motivated by the Latin root
caritas, love. As a result, we saw visitations by a Lady Bountiful
who was distantly involved, not in the geographic sense, but in the
important sense of commitment. The third stage is the unique
contribution of the individual as intervener. Finally, we go beyond
individual involvement to the involvement of a whole network of
community groups. These groups form the base of support for
our programs; without their acceptance, we cannot succeed over
the long pull of time.

All of these stages have validity, but just as mental health programs are evolving toward a community focus, so also must our
volunteer efforts. If we arrive at stage one or two and consider

---

*Director, State of Illinois Department of Mental Health, 160 North LaSalle Street,
Chicago, Ill.

5

that we are doing all we can, the evolutionary process we seek will never become reality. The movement toward community mental health services says, implicitly and explicitly: "Help us seek out patients. Help us treat them. Help us rehabilitate them." When we involve the community in helping persons among us who are sick, we find that this involvement produces a healthier community. But our message must be *more* than this. In my opinion, we must say to the prospective patient: "Let us work together to prevent your illness," or better still, "Let us help you to become healthier, more mature, more comfortable."

That volunteer citizens do not need glamourous settings in which to serve, is well borne out by response to the Peace Corps, and more recently, to President Johnson's appeal for volunteers in the War on Poverty. We have seen amazing response to hard, dirty, thankless jobs. In the mental health field, jobs are no less difficult, and the sense of gratification can be immense.

We need to consider the use of volunteering as a leisure-time activity. Soon we may see 10 to 20 per cent of the population supporting 80 to 90 per cent who do not need to work, or for whom work will not be available. I have read that an efficient tomato-picking machine will soon be in use in such volume that it will be doing the work of fifty-six thousand men in California alone. In the field of microelectronics, it may be cheaper to throw away electronic components than to repair them. In one giant step go the maintenance men and perhaps the TV repair men. Either we are going to have more volunteers or more patients. To prevent illness, much will depend on how well we use volunteers.

We must realize that citizen volunteers often can become better spokesmen and interpreters of our programs than professional persons. While there are many professional persons who are able and willing to explain concepts, community attitudes may not allow the patient or community to accept a professional point of view. The volunteer can be a bridge between the patient, the community and the hospital. He can provide resources and approaches that are outside time limits of professional staff.

Volunteering teaches volunteers about the mental health movement, and through them, significant segments of the community become informed. As a result, the sociopolitical support for mental health programs is strengthened. Volunteering also defines the moral responsibility of the community in that an individual's responsibility for his neighbor becomes more than a worthy aspiration. Perhaps the most important therapeutic aspect of volunteer work is its ability to humanize the dehumanizing but sometimes necessary aspects of our current methods.

I advocate a comprehensive integrated view of the term volunteer as against segmenting terms such as *hospital volunteer* or *direct service volunteer* or *indirect service volunteer* which we now use. For example, let us consider a program which would assign volunteers to individual patients and their relatives *at the point where the professional is first aware that an individual needs help.* One example of this kind of support is being carried out in Springfield, Illinois, where mental health association volunteers drop in and visit with relatives of each new patient who has entered nearby Jacksonville State Hospital. Even this isn't early enough, and it is not complete enough. At the very start of treatment, volunteers can make informative visits to relatives, and perhaps to school teachers, employers, and ministers. They can be trained to be helpful and they can bring literature with information about mental illness and recovery.

We are now encouraging the physician who is a general practitioner to continue his interest in a patient from the initial attempt to help, right on through hospitalization and aftercare. I recommend that we consider setting up some experimental programs around the *general service volunteer,* a volunteer who could be encouraged and trained to work with a patient from the start to the finish of his period of incapacity.

The value of such a generalist approach has been demonstrated in the Indiana Mental Health Association's *adopt-a-patient* program, aimed at so-called *forgotten patients.* In this program forty-five hundred *volunteer generalists* are asked to do anything they can on behalf of patients. I suggest that generalist volunteers can be assigned to help the patient and his relatives *before* the patient becomes forgotten.

We must ask ourselves this: Can the volunteer do something therapeutic for the patient which need not be reserved for our professional guilds? The answer is clearly, yes. In enlarging the scope of volunteer activities, let us not dilute our professional standards. But neither let us use professional standards to ward off every new idea and approach.

Competent supervision for clearly defined roles will permit volunteers to become members of the therapeutic team in a co-ordinated mental health effort. We have learned that volunteers want training, supervision, and direction. They want to have a choice in the kind of work they will do, and to understand the goals of service they will give. Put another way, role clarification and role satis-faction are two essentials. Often we find that individuals are trig-gered to volunteer by a charitable impulse. But this impulse is useless unless we prepare the individual for a role, letting him go and also letting him grow. These are critical areas: how we train our volunteers and how far we are really interested in letting them grow.

Historically, the volunteer related his activities to a charitable motive, one of giving his time to a cause. Today, we must relate them to the survival of individuals in our society. The Lady Bounti-ful approach will ill-prepare volunteers for realities in which they will function. If they are to be more than coffee pourers, they must come close to people they serve and see the patient not as they hope he will be, but as he actually is. They will become depressed unless they have been prepared, not for an expectation of success, but for one of serving. Those they serve will not always be grateful. They will not always understand. Out of the expectation of direct gratification, we can only expect hopelessness.

For volunteers, there must be an understanding of both patient and staff. The volunteer should be trained to understand the pro-fessional role, the team approach, the treatment process. The root of such training should be in dialogue. We should not give volun-teers a slight orientation and then expect them to do an assigned job, to sign in and out and to keep their mouths shut. We should allow them a chance to become generalists in the sense that, as they progress and mature in their undertakings, they can broaden their vistas. We should institute a strong feedback mechanism so that, by being able to give candid reactions, volunteers and perhaps staff, have the chance to grow. I prefer to call a training period *therapeutic involvement,* whereby volunteers see the therapeutic process evolving, not to emulate it, but to understand it.

The volunteer should, unlike our maxims of the past, become involved. He should show favoritism. He should relate spontaneously to patients. Well-motivated volunteers can do this only with proper preparation, with endorsement of professional staff, and with opportunity for dialogue with peers who happen to be professionally trained. Volunteers are not a threat to professional staff. They will not water down professional standards. They have a unique contribution to make. Volunteers represent a community orientation that is also reality-oriented. The therapy they can offer as generalists ranges from helping patients shop, finding and setting up apartments, getting to know local merchants, reaching employers, and countless other undertakings. Yet, it is only the non-threatened and mature professional who can allow volunteers this growth potential.

We should make it clear that the volunteer need not be an amateur. A lay person may be trained toward a role as professional as that of a salaried employee. On the other hand, a volunteer may already have professional mental health training. As we look for volunteers for community mental health services, let us take a fresh look at the potential of active or retired mental health personnel. For example, in Michigan a state-wide educational program is staffed by cadres of retired social workers, psychologists, nurses, and physicians. After a tailored refresher training course, these people put on mental health education and training programs for police officers, nurses, ministers, teachers, and physicians. These professional volunteers may also be a resource for counseling or other direct work with patients.

We should expand and capitalize on experience we have had in using professional talent from fields other than mental health. We should try to get businessmen to use their ability where it counts, as advisors to governmental agencies in management, or as advisors and helpers in the business affairs of patients. A reporter may serve more effectively in a mental health education capacity than in direct contact with patients. An attorney might be more effective in mental health education with judges, police officers and fellow attorneys, or in behalf of a patient's legal affairs. A designer might create a layout for a mental health week award or new furniture designs for patient centers. A management consultant might supervise staff training programs. A tradesman who is retired might teach his skill to patients. All these things have been done. Too frequently they are hit-and-miss developments rather than planned activities within the framework of a consistent policy.

We must use volunteers in the full area of potential service, as aides in prevention, as well as during treatment and rehabilitation. For example, in one clinic the facilities were swamped by couples having marital difficulties. It became apparent that their troubles were not so much emotional problems as money problems. The agency set up a volunteer financial clinic made up of a banker and a lawyer to help clients organize their money affairs. This was real prevention, made possible only through the help of volunteer citizens of the community.

In Illinois we are creating community-centered jobs to be filled by paid staff. Volunteers can act as aides to these professional staff people in any number of ways. We are going to hire and train people in the community who will act as a resource for disorganized persons, as a guide to welfare, rehabilitation, employment or mental health programs which might help an individual in crisis and near the point of breakdown. We will call such a person an *intervener*. He or she will perform a valuable community service in the complex business of seeing to it that the individual in crisis actually gets the help it takes to *prevent* his falling to pieces.

In another job, staff will follow up a patient's adjustment and achievements in the community. Often a patient or former patient just wants to know whether or not he is doing all right and how he compares with others in performance. This staff member will give valuable support. Or perhaps he will hear from the family that the patient really isn't doing too well. He can then evaluate the risk and without all the emotional complications of the family's making the decision, suggest that a patient come in and see the psychiatrist or even return to the hospital.

We will shortly hire six paid workers from the heavily populated Woodlawn area of Chicago to commute back and forth from the two Woodlawn wards at Manteno State Hospital, about forty-five miles south of Chicago. The paid workers will organize about sixty volunteers in each neighborhood who will be block leaders. They will be anchors in the community to work with patients in the hospital and back home in the neighborhood: in stores, churches, clubs, street corners, yes, even taverns, so that patients will move back to community life more easily.

I have mentioned some areas in the community where new department staff may well work with volunteer aides. Here is another example: in a tough Chicago district there were several store front churches whose ministers and parishioners were anxious to do what they could for mental health. They were not highly educated and since most had full-time day jobs, they were available only in the evening. Still, we couldn't afford to waste that kind of willingness. What we did was to organize the women into a baby-sitting service and the men into a motor pool so that neighborhood mothers could get to outpatient clinics in the evening and back home safely.

Finally, let me say that in volunteer activities the biblical counsel, "In giving we also receive," holds true. We live in a society that is rapidly becoming dehumanized in many ways. One example is giving charity to one's fellow men. You can give by a simple payroll deduction and contribute to hundreds of different problems that you never see. But as a volunteer the individual does see the problem, and it makes him healthier by giving him a significant mission in life.

Chapter 2

THE DEVELOPMENT OF A VOLUNTEER PROGRAM IN A COMMUNITY MENTAL HEALTH CLINIC

ANNE UMANA VARGUS, A.C.S.W.*

AT THE Greater Lawrence Guidance Center[1] we have attempted to integrate volunteers into our total service program. The Center serves one core city with three surrounding towns in northeastern Massachusetts, encompassing a population of nearly one hundred thirty-five thousand people. It is supported by state and local tax funds, the local United Fund, modest fees and generous donations. In addition to direct clinic services, based on crisis-focused treatment, the Center provides consultation to persons whose daily work is concerned with the mental health of children and adults. Mental health education is provided for the local professional community and for the lay public. Its goal is to promote understanding of the clinic's functions, philosophy, and relationship to total mental health needs of the community.

In this geographical area, the Clinic is unique in that most of its original staff were residents of the Greater Lawrence area. Today it has twenty-four staff members, fifteen of whom live in the area served by the Clinic. The founders and board of directors of the Clinic represent the various levels, economic and cultural, of the

---

[1] The author wishes to acknowledge the invaluable assistance of Mary D. Bain, M.D., Psychiatric Director of the Greater Lawrence Guidance Center, Inc., in the writing of this paper.

*Chief of Volunteer Services
Greater Lawrence Guidance Center
217 Haverhill Street
Lawrence, Mass.

total community and of the different structures within it. This group of citizens is committed to the improvement of their community and is vitally interested in the growth of the Center.

HISTORY OF THE VOLUNTEER PROGRAM

Prior to establishment of our current volunteer program, individuals had occasionally been recruited to assist staff with various time-limited projects. Volunteer service was given further impetus when the Center's auxiliary, the *Friends,* was formed in 1962. Within two years, the chairman of the volunteer committee of the *Friends,* despite obvious progress of her program, had begun to state with conviction that the future of volunteer activities could not be assured unless professional staff were made available for direction and supervision.

The integration and coordination of a program cannot be an overnight occurrence. Hence, the actualization of our program followed many years of thinking and planning by the psychiatric director and board. Recruiting for a mental health specialist for the position of chief of volunteer services began, and in November, 1964, a certified psychiatric social worker was appointed.

PREPARATION

Of key importance in initial planning were meetings of the chief of volunteer service with the *Friends'* volunteer chairman to discuss previous activities, plans, expectations, problems, ideas and potential volunteers. The volunteer chairman was a valuable resource, sharing her judgment of volunteers and her knowledge of the community of which she had been a long-time resident.

The chief of volunteer services held conferences with each staff member to exchange ideas about the volunteer role, administration of the volunteer program, and potential areas of volunteer assignment.

Weekly conferences have been held between the psychiatric director and chief of volunteer services, for review of clinic services and ideas and plans for volunteers within these services. A *Request for Volunteer Service* form was designed for use by staff. A *Volunteer Orientation Course* was arranged. A *Volunteer Application* form was devised. A *time card* for statistical purposes was approved.

SERVICES TO BE OFFERED

Our initial study of services to be performed by volunteers was by no means considered final or conclusive since growth of a well-planned volunteer service should parallel expansion of the clinic and its skill in utilizing volunteer services. *Indirect services* include writing for our newsletter, typing, filing, stenographing, addressographing, and bookkeeping. *Direct services* include automobile escorts; individual or group sessions for tutoring or cultural enrichment; formation of relationships with emotionally deprived people. Requests are made for *Direct Service* by recommendation of the clinical team.

Waiting-room assistants were needed not only to relieve the receptionist but to provide activity for children who regularly accompanied family members to clinic appointments. It was felt that formation of healthy relationships could be a preventive measure for children who are part of a constellation in crisis.

RECRUITMENT

Once we had established a genuine need for volunteers, we began recruiting from the *Friends'* mailing list. From seven hundred members, approximately sixty women responded of whom a small number were available at that time. As staff requests for service increased, we recruited from high schools, private academies, colleges, and secretarial associations in our community. Church, P.T.A., social groups and individuals expressed interest in our program. We also applied for a *Commonwealth Service Corps* program of ten youth volunteers. (See Chapter 3.)

Despite expressions of group interest, all recruiting has been carried out individually. This approach permits careful selection of persons for potential assignments and allows a thorough explanation of the program, the role of the volunteer, and the methods to be used. This recruiting process strengthened the Clinic's ties and broadened our base within the community.

There are many untapped resources in a community for volunteer activity. One exciting program at the Center has been provided by a local actors' group. A staff psychologist suggested that a well-known mental health play might be presented by volunteers for his teachers' seminar. When the chief of volunteer services talked with the theatrical group about volunteering their time, the group welcomed an opportunity to perform a community service. The evening was a tremendous success; in fact, a neighboring community clinic requested the same presentation as the highlight of their annual board meeting.

Another exciting volunteer endeavor has been the program for children with perceptual motor difficulties. This program is staffed by ten volunteers trained and supervised by our language retraining consultant. These ten volunteers have begun a two-year course of study which includes theory and practice. The project has not only been successful in terms of volunteer participation and satisfaction; it has provided the Center with a service heretofore almost unavailable in our community. These are illustrations of how volunteers can provide extra services and benefits not possible within operating resources.

ORIENTATION

A volunteer who has been accepted by the Clinic needs orientation to her new undertaking. Staff who requested her assistance may also wish to review their ideas and expectations for her work. Orientation of staff and volunteer is a continuing process based on turnover of personnel, growth of services, and introduction of volunteers into new areas.

Our initial orientation course for volunteers ran two hours a week for seven weeks. The course was open to all applicants. Many persons were interested in taking the course for their own knowledge, others attended in order to satisfy a pressing need for companionship, others because of intellectual curiosity. We felt that all who attended were potential missionaries who could convey information to the community regarding the purposes and programs of the Clinic. Some who began the course dropped out after the initial sessions. This attrition process was interpreted as a healthy self-screening mechanism.

From those who completed the course came the basic corps of volunteers. The orientation had served several purposes. It enhanced the volunteers' identification with goals of the agency; it instilled a feeling of belonging necessary for good *esprit de corps;* it provided observational opportunity for the chief of volunteer services who attended each session. During the course, she began evaluation of individual volunteers and scheduled screening interviews.

Subject matter of the course was focused on philosophy, departmental structure, and staff of the Center; current mental health issues; description of people who receive service from the Center; the meaning of illness and its relationship to the family constellation and community; functions of other community agencies and resources; use and importance of the interpersonal relationship, and the role of the volunteer within the Center. Each session was led by an appropriate staff person.

SELECTION

The selection of volunteers is a major responsibility of the chief of volunteer services. Interviews provide an excellent opportunity to clarify the Center's needs and services as well as rules and standards of performance for volunteers. For potential volunteers it is an opportunity to pursue doubts or questions. This interview serves to set the tone of the volunteer's future relationship with the Center.

The interviewer must sensitively explore motivation, attitudes, and interests; qualifications for a particular job; willingness to accept supervision. Volunteers interested in direct services must manifest warmth, understanding, and good judgment since their fundamental contribution is their own warmth, spontaneity and ability to relate.

PLACEMENT

Placement of the volunteer is a matching process, a utilization of our appraisal of the volunteer and the prerequisites of a particular assignment. Placement actually begins in the screening interview. For example, a dental hygienist, whose professional training would not find a place within the Center, may say that she always found pleasure in teaching children good dental care. She may prove to be an excellent remedial tutor. A very feminine mother of four boys may be delighted with the prospect of working with a culturally deprived five-year-old girl. In the placement interview, the chief of volunteer services should make clear the purpose and importance of an assignment, reassure the volunteer of her competence for the undertaking, and explain the resources arranged for her supervision.

SUPERVISION

If a volunteer is assigned to an area of indirect service, she is introduced to her supervisor, the business manager, during the placement interview. If a volunteer is to participate in direct service, she is introduced to the professional staff person who requested her services. This meeting initiates a relationship which is to continue in the following months. All volunteers giving direct service are supervised by a member of the professional staff.

Supervision of volunteers is a prime concern. It is here that a program distinguishes itself, for *supervision represents the focal investment of the agency sponsoring the program.* A volunteer internalizes this investment and, through the supervisory relationship, translates it into quality performance.

Volunteers need support, reassurance and encouragement in their performance. They need an opportunity to discuss and question. They need respect and dignity within the structure. Supervisory conferences with direct service volunteers are scheduled weekly and range from one-half hour to an hour depending on material and number of cases to be discussed.

Additional conferences are arranged bimonthly at which the volunteer, the patient's therapist, and the chief of volunteer services discuss cases. Initially, volunteers need to be supported, for they often feel inadequate in discussions with professional people. These conferences serve not only to communicate information, but also to cement relationships between volunteer and staff.

SUMMARY

Reported in this chapter is the historical development and planning of our volunteer program, and a description of the method of formulation, integration and coordination used. This program is ten months old and has seen more than four thousand seven-hundred hours of service. We are cognizant that our description and appraisal is largely subjective at this point and we look forward to objective research which may reveal weak spots and highlight strengths.

We anticipate a future of tremendous activity and qualitative and quantitative growth for this most exciting program.

Chapter 3

THE COMMONWEALTH SERVICE CORPS
A DOMESTIC PEACE CORPS FOR
MASSACHUSETTS

DAVID O. McGAVERN, M.S.W.*

BACKGROUND

On February 18, 1964, a study commission was appointed by Governor Endicott Peabody to determine whether major volunteer efforts could be directed toward unmet needs in the Commonwealth of Massachusetts. Over a two-month period, the commission members interviewed prominent people in the social welfare field.[1] A questionnaire concerning volunteer needs was sent to seven hundred and forty health, education, and welfare agencies throughout the state. In response to this questionnaire, two hundred and sixty agencies requested a minimum of seven thousand volunteers.

Armed with the study commission's report and a draft proposal of legislation, the Governor approached the legislature in joint session on May 12, 1964.[2]

The study commission had determined that there were indeed many critical areas of need for volunteers and that there were thousands of citizens in the Commonwealth who would be well qualified to serve as volunteers. They envisioned the Commonwealth Service Corps as a domestic Peace Corps. Their thinking was

*Supervisor, Area Program Analysts
Action for Boston Community Development
18 Tremont Street
Boston, Mass.
Formerly, Director of Selection, Commonwealth Service Corps

[1] Study Commission for the Commonwealth Service Corps was directed by Professor Lawrence Fuchs of Brandeis University.

[2] *Message of His Excellency, Governor Endicott Peabody, Delivered in a Joint Convention of the Two Houses, relative to the Establishment of a Commonwealth Service Corps Commission.* Senate, No. 838, Boston, May 12, 1964.

corroborated by the establishment of the federal program, *Volunteers in Service to America,* and Radcliffe College Alumnae Association's *New Opportunities for Women.* These programs represented a strong movement to utilize untapped talent to benefit the community.

The Commonwealth Service Corps was translated into legislation in May of 1964. By September of 1964, a director was appointed.[3] In December of the same year, the Service Corps became operational. By April of the following year the Service Corps had placed one hundred and forty volunteers in social welfare agencies throughout the state. In these placements, volunteers were working in a court clinic, in study halls for teenagers who could not study at home, with elderly in information centers, in workshops for the mentally retarded, prisons, and settlement houses.

The Commonwealth Service Corps evolved a philosophy concerning the recipient of services and the volunteer who renders services. This philosophy expresses the belief that the recipient of services can and must have a voice in determining how these services shall be provided, that any service program in which the recipients are not represented is not truly democratic. In practice, this means that a volunteer program in a mental hospital must have so-called mental patients serving in the program. It assumes that the client has a good idea of what is best for himself, that the individuals with whom the volunteer may be working are first and foremost dignified human beings who, for a span of time, have severe limitations on their opportunity for self-realization. This premise is in keeping with the federal government's antipoverty policy of involving the poor in the planning and implementation of programs.

ORGANIZATION

The statute of the Commonwealth Service Corps delineates three categories of volunteers. The first is comprised of full-time volunteers who work a minimum of thirty hours a week and are paid eighty dollars a month. Most people who apply for this position are either elderly persons who receive social security

---

[3] John C. Cort, Director, Commonwealth Service Corps.

benefits, or students who decide to drop out of college for a year and who usually have some independent income. We have found that mothers who are receiving aid to dependent children and who can earn an additional sum are another very good source of recruits. Fewer in number are people between the ages of twenty-five and fifty-five who have decided to give a year in service to their fellow man.

The second category is comprised of volunteers who work twelve hours a week and can be reimbursed for expenses such as travel and lunch. The people who fit this category tend to be housewives or working people.

The third category is known as student volunteers. They are required to serve a minimum of six hours a week and can receive payment of up to seventy-five cents an hour.

The question has often been asked whether a person is a volunteer if he receives money. We are attempting to demonstrate that money is not a deterrent to the spirit of volunteer service; indeed, it can command better service from volunteers. The legislation stipulating work hours is intended to assure the requesting agency that volunteers can be counted upon to provide the requisite service hours every week. In this way the agency can use a volunteer in a more effective way.

The prescribed manner for an agency to acquire Service Corps volunteers is submission of a proposal to the program department of the Commonwealth Service Corps. This proposal describes the agency, the projected use of volunteers, the hours of work, and the nature of supervision. The Service Corps determines the interest, challenge, and practicality of recruiting volunteers to work in that agency. The requesting agency often participates in recruiting volunteers to work in that agency. However, final selection of applicants is made by the Commonwealth Service Corps.

The Commonwealth Service Corps is at present funded entirely by state government. However, as agreed in the legislation, the Service Corps is currently searching for private and federal funds to supplement the state contribution. We have found that administrative overhead costs of running such a program are higher than originally anticipated. These costs amount to about 40 per cent of our total budget.

PERSONNEL

The Commonwealth Service Corps has two functions: (1) to render technical assistance to municipalities who are applying for Economic Opportunity funds and (2) to administer volunteer services. The organization is divided into five regions covering the state. In each region, there is a director who has responsibility for developing programs in his area. In the City of Boston there is a central office which lends support to the regions.

A volunteer in the field is responsible to the agency in which he works, then to the Service Corps regional director and finally to the central office. We have found that identification with the Service Corps is maintained through training, orientation to Service Corps principles, and follow-up support in the field, all of which are necessary to continued high quality of service.

The process of selecting volunteer applicants is not a complex one.[4] However, with limited staff and an overwhelming number of applicants, there are sometimes delays in fitting a suitable person to a project at a location convenient to his home.

The rate of rejection is about 20 per cent. This figure is low for a very good reason: the nature of the agency's business attracts a particular kind of individual. Those rejected are clearly told why they cannot be used and are often referred to other volunteer agencies.

The Service Corps feels that training is an absolute necessity in preparing a volunteer to work in a social welfare agency. Since funds for training were not allocated in the original budget, training has occurred primarily in the host agency. We anticipate that in the future all volunteers may be trained by the Service Corps with the host agency participating. We feel that the volunteer should have an outside, objective look at the social welfare scene as well as some education concerning the agency in which he will work.

MENTAL HEALTH PROGRAMS

Approximately 10 per cent of the Service Corps programs are devoted to projects in mental health and related areas. The Service Corps has a number of projects planned, completed, or currently

---

[4] McGavern, D.O.: Guides for volunteer selection. Boston, Commonwealth Service Corps, July, 1965.

operating in mental health clinics, state hospitals, psychiatric units in general hospitals, state schools for the retarded, mental health associations, associations for retarded children or young adults, and related agencies. Space does not permit full description of every program, but three or four examples will give the reader an idea.

At Fernald State School, twenty-two Service Corpsmen were involved in a unique and experimental program in which five college corpsmen lived on the ward and were responsible for overseeing educational and recreational activities of thirty patients and seventeen high school corpsmen. The program was designed to illustrate the impact that young, intelligent people can have on a state school.

At the South Shore Mental Health Center in Quincy, Massachusetts, ten corpsmen have been working with juvenile first offenders in group activities such as shop training, *Junior Achievement,* and gymnasium activities. This project was one of the original pilot projects of the Service Corps and it has been very successful.

At the Worcester Youth Guidance Center, corpsmen are working with retarded and emotionally disturbed people. They are leading activity clubs, conducting weekly special events, serving as readers with daycare patients, working in daily outdoor programs, and helping in sheltered workshops. Many of these corpsmen are employed full time and are paid eighty dollars a month.

At the Massachusetts Association for Mental Health, one full-time corpsman is working as a teacher-supervisor for convalescent mental patients who are doing clerical work at the association's office. There is a possibility that this program may be expanded in the near future.

For the fall of 1965, there are approximately sixteen mental health programs in which Service Corpsmen will be working. While the problems are many, the Service Corps recognizes that service agencies have a need for volunteers that is unlikely to diminish. We are glad to contribute in meeting that need.

Part II

DEVELOPING PROGRAMS FOR LONG-HOSPITALIZED PERSONS

Chapter 4

THE CHANGING STATE HOSPITAL: WHAT IT NEEDS FROM VOLUNTEERS

ROBERT C. HUNT, M.D.*

F OR SEVERAL years there has been a sharp disparity among leaders in psychiatry as to the ultimate fate of the state hospitals. At one pole are those holding influential opinions who agree with Doctor Harry Solomon, past president of the American Psychiatric Association, that the large state hospital is bankrupt beyond remedy and should be liquidated. This group is confident that large hospitals can be eliminated during our lifetime and with our present tools. At the other pole are those who believe that alternatives to the state hospital system are unproven, that premature commitment to them may wreck the state hospitals which, with all their handicaps, are still the main resource for the majority of the mentally ill.

Regardless of their ultimate fate, there is agreement that for the next few years state hospitals will continue as the major resource for severe mental illness and retardation, and that they should be helped to improve their services. This concept has been embodied in the Hospital Improvement Program of the National Institute of Mental Health.

In 1962, as staff began planning this program, they wanted to know more of what was happening in state hospitals around the country. They wanted to know what constituted improvement in actual practice in order to evaluate applications for improvement grants. As a result, it was my good fortune to visit a number of the best state hospitals all over the United States for the National Institute of Mental Health.

*State of New York, Department of Mental Hygiene
119 Washington Avenue
Albany, New York

On starting this tour I was immediately impressed with the variety of ferment, innovation and movement, with the tremendous range of good ideas being carried out with imagination and enthusiasm. This was by no means limited to well-known front runners; many an unknown, unpublicized hospital was found to be pioneering most creatively.

It has seemed to me that we can group all of the changes taking place in hospital practice into five major trends or characteristics.

The first of these is a general humanizing of the atmosphere. Over the past ten years, there has been a tremendous revolution within state hospitals, a revolution in our conception of what a patient is, of what a hospital is for, of staff-patient relationships, and of patient behavior. The most striking manifestation of this new conception is the open ward policy, the unlocking of doors so that patients are free to make many of their own decisions, and are expected to be responsible for much of their own life. This humanizing of the atmosphere shows itself in multiple ways which may seem small to us but are very important to patients: the kind of clothing they wear, the kind of eating utensils provided, the regulations about wearing glasses and fraternizing with the opposite sex. A thousand and one aspects of daily life are revolutionized when patients are seen in this new light.

The second major characteristic is the unit system, the attempt to break up a large institution into smaller functioning units. This does not mean a special building for ambulatory aged or a special ward for disturbed young females, but rather small all-purpose divisions. Unit systems come in many shapes and sizes. There is the type with a geographic base, as in the Clarinda Plan. Clarinda State Hospital's catchment area is divided into smaller regions of one or two counties each. Each of these regions has a unit in the hospital which houses its long-term patients, admits all of its new patients, and works with the agencies of its county on screening prospective admissions, aftercare, and community mental health programs. In effect, there are multiple small hospitals within the Clarinda State Hospital, each serving its own district.

Another approach to the unit system is to assign new patients to different units in rotation without regard to geographic origin. This method, while not providing the relationship to community agencies, as with the geographic plan, does provide advantages of the unit system within the hospital.

These unit systems seem to work well for patients, but I am not sure why. Perhaps one factor is our expectations. In traditional hospitals we had elaborate classification of wards to house categories of patient behavior. The patient on a disturbed ward was expected to be disturbed; the one on a regressed ward was expected to be incontinent: everyone around him was. In small units there are not enough regressed patients to form a separate grouping. They are mingled with the others, are expected to behave much like the others, and they almost invariably do.

A third characteristic of improvement is a focus on rehabilitation of chronic patients. This shows itself in many ways: better housing, clothing, food, recreation; many projects for active intervention by remotivation and intensive treatment; various methods of vocational rehabilitation. One of the most exciting developments is the use of hospital industry as a genuinely therapeutic tool. The project at Medfield State Hospital in Massachusetts, originally supported by a National Institute of Mental Health grant, has been most impressive in results achieved with a very difficult group of patients. A number of hospitals have also gotten good results using sheltered workshops as at Metropolitan State Hospital. (See Chapter 7.)

The fourth major trend is development of specialized programs for specialized groups, such as children, geriatric patients, alcoholics, drug addicts and acting-out character disorders. These programs are likely to occur in hospitals which have active treatment and rehabilitation programs for the general hospital population. If all patients are under maximum security with little treatment, it does not matter how they are mixed together. With an active treatment program it becomes apparent that certain groups with special needs do not do well in a generalized program.

The fifth major trend is leadership in developing community treatment of the mentally ill. More and more state hospitals are participating in preadmission screening as at Boston State Hospital. Boston's *Home Treatment Service* is another approach to community treatment, and a number of hospitals around the country are trying similar devices. Many hospitals either operate outpatient clinics or have helped other agencies to develop these services. Everywhere there is use of partial hospitalization by day treatment, night treatment, halfway houses. Perhaps the most common program is aftercare, which is an ancient tradition in some states but is only beginning in others. Quite commonly, the first step in a community treatment program is to start aftercare so that more patients can be moved out of the hospital. A few hospitals have pioneered in developing comprehensive community programs. Interest in comprehensive programs is increasing now that there are federal funds for centers.

The five trends above do not include intensive treatment of newly admitted patients. I went to the better hospitals, and asked them what they had which was new and different: these better hospitals have had a rather good level of treatment for new patients for at least ten years and it does not occur to them to point this out as particularly significant. Yet I am sure that many innovations become possible only when there is first a good treatment service.

Is there any common denominator to these characteristics? I have some thoughts about this. One is that the *fact of innovation* is more central than the specific innovations carried out. There are many state hospitals in which change is a way of life. We do not hear a word about inertia, about how hard it is to get permission from higher headquarters to go ahead with some idea. This says something about leadership given by the superintendent and about attitudes all the way down to the ward level. It also says something about leadership at the state level, what it permits and encourages and rewards.

Another thought is that for new ideas to work they must grow out of the thinking of people who are doing the job. A striking thing about the unit system, for instance, is that it seems to have arisen spontaneously in many places from people's own thinking. Many claim that they never heard of Clarinda or say that they only heard vaguely about it. It is a discouraging business to try selling an idea to people who are not yet ready for it. It is much more effective if the idea evolves out of their own needs.

All of these changes should cause us to take a look at what they mean for volunteer services.

The volunteer program in state hospitals began at a time, fifteen to twenty years ago, when we saw a patient and his needs very differently from the way we do today. We saw the patient as a shut-in who needed Lady Bountiful to bring a ray of sunshine from the outside world. In a modern state hospital there are scarcely any shut-ins, and no real place for Lady Bountiful.

We saw the patient as a dependent ward inhabitant, spending virtually his whole life on the ward, with no resources or activities other than those scheduled for him. He had a lot of idle time on the ward, so it made sense to bring in volunteers for group parties.

I had an embarrassing time eight years ago when a couple of the old faithful members of the volunteer corps came to me all upset because they had put on their regular ward party and nobody came to it. The ward had been unlocked and patients for the first time had a choice. They were not a captive audience, and they had chosen to do other things. In a *modern* state hospital you see very few patients when you walk through the wards in the daytime; they are all out somewhere else, in treatment or at some occupational or recreational activity, or on a work assignment, shopping, visiting friends or playing pinochle.

We used to see patients as very delicate, fragile beings in danger of a serious setback from a thoughtless word. So we had to be cautious about who was allowed to come in contact with them. Volunteers had to be screened and selected carefully. Then we trained them, with a great many hours of lectures about psychiatric illness and the behavior to be expected of patients, and the rules and regulations, and the do's and don'ts and admonitions and the warnings. There were also orthodox dogmas about the kinds of jobs that must never be given to a volunteer and kinds of wards that no volunteer should be allowed on. What nonsense! The trouble is, a lot of people started programs without knowing these rules, and got away with it for years before they found out about the rules, and then it was too late; their programs had been working without the rules.

There is literally not a single type of task or function that has not been done well by volunteers somewhere, sometime. In most programs, screening of volunteers has become pretty perfunctory. Some of the best volunteer work has been done by patients, both present and former patients. For many types of volunteer work detailed training may do more harm than good if the training focuses on mental illness. In much of this work we don't want the volunteer to deal with illness or with a *patient,* but rather with a *person.* The fact that this person is also a patient should be virtually irrelevant in many relationships with volunteers.

So volunteer programs are tending to move from emphasis on large parties toward work with small groups and with individuals. The student volunteer movement (which was conceived, born and developed in Boston) emphasizes work with individuals. There is movement away from standardized general programs toward more specialized activities to fit specialized skills, interests, needs.

Thus it may happen that a new volunteer's interest is in raising flowers, so we find a group of patients who have the same interest and would enjoy a garden club. Or there is a patient who wants to learn Spanish, possibly has a real need for this in the job she expects to have after discharge, so we look for a volunteer who can teach Spanish, and other patients who want to join the class. It is in the very nature of such an *ad hoc* project that it tends to be temporary. When you have an atmosphere which encourages this kind of innovation, there is always something new coming along to take its place.

Volunteer movements seem to be floundering in the face of the unit system. At least I have not come across any examination of the implications of the unit system for recruitment, training, and assignment of volunteers. Hospitals I have seen with a good unit system don't seem to be using very much volunteer service. This may be coincidence, but it may not.

We should do some soul-searching as to whether the original type of volunteer program *should* survive. Long-term shut-in patients are going out of style. Hospitals which are using to the full our best techniques for treatment and rehabilitation, which are bringing these to bear on the greatest number of patients, are changing very rapidly. They are becoming much more like acute treatment centers, much less like custodial institutions. Acute treatment is becoming a much shorter process than it used to be; large numbers of old-time patients have been moved out; hardly any new cases are being fed into the chronic population.

We are in the midst of a revolution, moving care and treatment of the mentally ill out of institutions and into the community. So I suggest that if the volunteer movement with the mentally ill has a future, that future is not in hospitals as much as out in the community. Some moves in that direction have been made and I hear that in Massachusetts there are volunteers in clinics. (See Chapter 2.) But I have heard of no one who has visualized the time when nearly all patients who use volunteer services will be in their own homes or in nursing and boarding homes. There, they will often have problems and handicaps and disabilities and loneliness. I am sure we will see the day when my kind of work and yours is almost entirely outside of institutions. I wish you would hurry, because I want to see this come about in my lifetime.

Chapter 5

COORDINATION OF VOLUNTEER SERVICES WITH OTHER DEPARTMENTS IN A MENTAL HOSPITAL

WILLIAM E. NETH*

I N LARGE STATE mental hospitals, the department of volunteer services and the individual volunteer will relate in some way to the total hospital staff. *Total hospital staff* bears repeating because in mental health volunteering there is often a subtle snobbery which implies that, like the Lodges and God, the volunteer speaks only to professional staff. Here, we shall consider staff to be everyone employed by an institution.

The formal organization of the hospital defines responsibilities and operations of each department: according to the interest of the hospital's executives and past contributions of volunteers, the department of volunteer services is assigned a place on the organization chart. This designation, however, is no guarantee that volunteer services will be integrated and coordinated with other departments.

The value of volunteer services must be demonstrated not only to the administration but particularly to the ward personnel. Many of these people hold the allegiance of their peers, have means for getting things done, and are often the first resource available to a volunteer on the ward. These individuals along with other employees from any profession or department may be called the "informal organization."

Although nonprofessional personnel are seldom involved in pro-

*Community Coordinator
Massachusetts Commission for the Aging
19 Milk Street
Boston, Mass.
Formerly, the author was Director of Volunteer Services, Boston State Hospital.

gram-planning or volunteer orientation, they are relied upon by professional staff to serve well. A director of volunteers will wisely be acquainted with the "informal organization" and encourage a mutually supporting relationship between these individuals and volunteers.

The investment made by the "informal organization" long before volunteers arrived should not be underrated. Even now in many hospitals, nurses, attendants and other employees work as volunteers in addition to their regular duties. Under great handicaps, sometimes without official leadership, these people have nurtured what have been called "growing edges," ideas with vitality which grow at the edge of the daily routine and at the right moment become full-blown. Then noticeable changes take place in the ward or building.

Among the hospital personnel may be found many ideas and projects which may well be the new frontiers for volunteer services. At one large hospital, for example, patients are encouraged by ward personnel to do volunteer work for the community. Although most of this activity has been limited to the wards, community volunteers could develop opportunities for patients to serve in the community. By assisting in the nurture of these "growing edges," volunteers can become integrated with the hospital system.

Relating to both the formal and informal organization is no easy task for any department in a psychiatric setting; it is doubly hard for the department of volunteer services. There is no frame of reference commonly understood by staff about the contribution, place, or value of the volunteer. Schools and colleges give the professions little information about volunteers; job descriptions and interviews seldom mention them; few in-service training programs include the volunteer as a therapeutic agent.

Consequently the department of volunteer services must prove itself, and in so doing, create an acceptable frame of reference. This is accomplished if volunteers are available where action is needed. Out of action centered around mutual interest in the patient will grow a relationship between volunteers, professional staff, and the informal organization. Volunteers must be available to seize possibilities which unexpectedly present themselves. How often the professional's efforts are thwarted because some turning point in the patient's life occurs when no one is available at that moment to act. Similarly, ward personnel may request service which only volunteers can give. Here, *in action,* volunteers are of enormous value to the patient and most welcomed by the staff.

Involvement with the "informal organization," action by the volunteer, and a clear relationship with professional staff are perhaps the primary components for coordination of volunteer services with other hospital departments. It is unwise to deal with these components separately. Rather than relating the volunteer only to professional staff, an effort should be directed toward upgrading the skills of ward staff. Supervision of volunteers and nonprofessional personnel at the same time will certainly reduce threatening feelings, misunderstanding, and the subtle snobbery often implied. More important, this is coordination and integration which gives rise to the freedom essential for action by volunteers.

Chapter 6

EXPLORATIONS OF THE VOLUNTEER ROLE: THE CASE AIDE PROGRAM AT BOSTON STATE HOSPITAL

VICTOR A. GELINEAU, Ph.D.*

A t Boston State Hospital, volunteers have been recruited to work as case aides in an experimental program with chronic psychotic patients.[1] The Boston State Case Aide Program extends customary volunteer functions, building upon the staff's many years of experience with Harvard and Radcliffe student volunteers. Its purposes are fourfold:

(1) to bring about *discharge* of patients who can successfully return to the community if they are given sufficient attention;

(2) to *prevent chronicity* in patients who without support might become chronically ill;

(3) *to strengthen the flow of communication and mutual concern between hospital and community;*

(4) *to alleviate the severe mental health manpower shortage* by creative use of volunteers.

To accomplish these goals the Case Aide Program has recruited volunteers from three segments of the population: students from colleges and universities; retired men and women who have useful skills and experience; adult volunteers who can bring to the program both maturity and vigor.

THE NEED FOR VOLUNTEERS

In recent decades, the ability of large public mental hospitals

*Consultant Coordinator, Case Aide Program
  Boston State Hospital
  591 Morton Street
  Boston, Mass.
[1] This grant was received from the Permanent Charity Fund of Boston.

35

to return patients to the community has greatly increased. However, because of shortages in facilities and personnel many patients remain in our hospitals even though they have a capacity for rehabilitation. In many hospitals, a backlog of these patients spends years on wards with insufficient staff to give them attention they need. Even though hospital personnel may be dedicated and skilled, they cannot work with all patients who could profit by individual attention.

Experience has shown that volunteers under supervision of trained professional persons can work directly with these patients, effecting a considerable change in their condition and helping them to move from the hospital to the community.

Since we cannot expect any large increment in the number of trained hospital workers, volunteers are one of the best resources available to help long-hospitalized patients and to free hospital personnel for other therapeutic efforts.[2-6]

PROGRESS OF THE CASE AIDE PROGRAM TO DATE

Professional personnel of this program include a part-time coordinator and several part-time psychiatric social workers who act as case aide supervisors. The total number of volunteers now working directly with patients is eighty-seven. For supervisory purposes, the volunteers are organized into groups of eight-to-twelve, under leadership of a social worker. The first group began work with patients in February, 1964, and in the following months, seven more groups were added.

In less than two years, the results have been good. To summarize some of the progress made to date, our experience shows the following:

    1. Volunteers are available in the adult population of greater

[2] Beck, J.C., Kantor, D., and Gelineau, V.: Follow-up study of chronic psychotic patients 'treated' by college case-aid volunteers. *Amer J Psychiat, 120*:269-271, 1963.

[2] Greenblatt, M., and Kantor, D.: Student volunteer movement and the manpower shortage. *Amer J Psychiat, 118*:809-814, 1962.

[4] Kantor, D.: *Intervention into Multiple Patterns of Insularity in a Custodially Organized Mental Hospital.* Unpublished doctoral dissertation, Brandeis University, April, 1963.

[5] Umbarger, C.C., Dalsimer, J., Morrison, A., and Breggin, P.R.: *College Students in a Mental Hospital.* New York, Grune & Stratton, 1962.

[6] Gelineau, V., and Kantor, D.: Pro-social commitment among college students. *J Soc Issues 20*:112-130, 1964.

Boston who can learn to work effectively with psychotics.
2. Patients hospitalized for long periods of time can be helped by volunteers.
3. Volunteers working as case aides can be supervised on a part-time basis by professional persons, extending the resources of trained mental health manpower.

Volunteers have been able to place fifteen patients in various community settings ranging from halfway houses to foster families. Several other patients have been placed in the hospital's vocational rehabilitation program. (See Chapter 11.)

To place this summary in proper perspective, we must examine characteristics of the patients, the volunteers, the psychiatric social workers who supervise them, and the nature of the rehabilitation process that takes place.

THE PATIENTS

In evaluating the number of patients returned to the community during these first months, several factors must be taken into account. The first is time. Although the program is nearly in full operation, most volunteer groups have been working a relatively short time. Secondly, placements in the community for released mental patients, especially work placements, have to be developed rather than found. Finally, although all patients in the program have the capacity for reintegration into the community, they are chronic patients from whom rapid change cannot be expected. Therefore, taking these factors into consideration, our success rate to date has been encouraging and possibly will increase.

It should be borne in mind that these patients would not have a favorable prognosis by clinical standards. All of them have received some active psychiatric care and have not responded. All have been hospitalized for considerable lengths of time, often in more than one institution. The mean number of years of hospitalization for these patients is 12.8 years with the median falling at ten. The mean age of these patients is 49.6 and the range from twenty-five to eighty-five years.

In most cases, the patients have been diagnosed as schizophrenic. Many are abandoned by friends and families and have had no contact with the outside world for long periods of time. Their social skills and ability to perform adequate roles have atrophied during long institutionalization. Their vocational skills have become obsolete or inadequate. The staff-patient ratio is such that hospital personnel can work with only a small proportion of them. When they do bring patients to the point of discharge, they may not have time to make the additional arrangements necessary for a discharged patient to live in the community.

THE VOLUNTEERS

At present we have a range of volunteers including students, adults, and retired people: some are still in their adolescence; some in their sixties and seventies; most are between thirty and fifty years old. A variety of ethnic and social groups is represented. Some volunteers are professional workers such as school teachers and a physicist; others are housewives. There is a preponderance of persons who typically staff volunteer efforts in this country: the upper-middle class, college trained, middle-aged female.

Recruitment of volunteers for such an unusual program requires considerable effort. Contact with local mental health associations and other groups was made through the Massachusetts Association for Mental Health. Appeals have been made by radio, newspaper articles, and a brochure. Staff of the program have met with organizations and have acted as recruiting agents on an individual basis.

Some problems encountered in the recruiting process stem from stereotyped perceptions of mental illness and the mental hospital. Explanation of the program and emphasis upon the availability of guidance, supervision and support are effective in allaying these concerns. The fact that the program involves direct contact with individual patients arouses some anxiety, but can also become an advantage in attracting volunteers who would not be interested in less original work.

A continuing and imaginative effort must be maintained to encourage a flow of volunteers into the program. There is potentially a large reserve of volunteers in the metropolitan area but they must be carefully sought. Our experience has shown that sustained efforts can maintain a steady flow of volunteers to the program.

Although research to evaluate the program is still in the data-gathering stage, we have begun to form some idea of the characteristics of our volunteers as well as the nature of the volunteer-patient relationship and the gratifications and problems encountered in the volunteer's work.

Motivation to engage in this new enterprise varies greatly with individuals. Some volunteers are active because mental illness has occurred in their own families. They are aware of the severity and complexity of the problem and are motivated to learn and to help. These volunteers are dedicated workers who bring compassion and understanding to patients.

Others had acquaintance with behavioral science in college and are productively reactivating their interest. These women find an opportunity to exercise latent skills and are greatly stimulated by the intellectual content of their experience.

Still others have a close relative working in the field of mental health. They can be of service and at the same time find a common interest with a husband or children working in the field.

There is also a group who might be termed career-testers. These are married women with grown children, who are interested in training for a satisfying career. From this group some have already been recruited into the mental health professions.

Although at times there are problems, the volunteer-patient relationship is a productive and gratifying human situation. The volunteer brings, first of all, contact with the outside world. The volunteer draws upon his altruistic impulses: he gives freely of himself without pay, consistently and in a genuine manner. Volunteers get to know and to *like* patients as people, not cases. The rehabilitative value of this relationship can hardly be overestimated. It is a relationship which the professional, by virtue of his structured role, cannot have with a patient.

The volunteers, particularly adults, are able to get things done for patients in the world to which they are daily related. They often show remarkable imagination and tenacity in doing this. To cite only a few examples—one volunteer after being called to her dying mother's bedside in San Francisco, kept in touch with the supervisor by telephone to make certain that placement of her patient in the community was being properly carried out in her absence. Another went into the home of a patient's family where no staff person had been welcome and was able to reestablish a productive relation between the patient and her family. The volunteer accomplished this even though there were large ethnic and class differences between her and the family. Still another so persistently heckled public authorities that she managed to get a respectable allocation of money for clothes for her patient who was hesitating to accept employment because she was miserably dressed.

Patients' response to this volunteer friendship and dedication has been remarkable. For example, a fifty-three year old woman patient who had been quite paranoid said to her volunteer after a few months, "You know, you're the only one I can really talk to. I haven't seen a single one of the people I used to know when they put me in here seventeen years ago."

Another seventy-six year old patient came to a supervisor one day and excitedly announced. "Mrs. B., you know what, I'm going to the ball game on ladies' day! My volunteer is taking me." Her volunteer is seventy-four years old.

One volunteer who is a professional dance teacher, after several weeks of receiving little response from her patient, decided to attempt communication by nonverbal means. She expressed her concern and affection by dancing for her. This silent, untidy patient greeted her volunteer at their next meeting carefully groomed and smiling. She said, "Hello, dear!" and threw her arms around her volunteer.

Incidents like these, which often symbolize the first step back to the human community, demonstrate the terrible need that volunteers are so generously filling.

Volunteers react in a variety of ways to the case aide experience. However, some regularities can be observed.

Volunteers soon become involved with the effort to help patients. Their supervision guides them in using this involvement effectively. Volunteers perceive the program as a learning experience, both intellectual and emotional. They feel they are learning a great deal about mental illness. An empathy develops with the patients and a more subtle understanding of the continuum between health and illness. We have also instituted a series of seminars which give intellectual content to their work.

Volunteers emphasize the importance to them of professional

supervision: to guide them through the experience; to teach them about the hospital, the patients, and mental illness generally, and to help them handle their own feelings. They feel that under these conditions the experience is one of growth.

For all volunteers, there is an initial period of anxiety which requires professional support to overcome. There is then a period of enthusiasm and exuberance while early progress can be seen. Later, when the severity of chronic psychosis is fully realized, the volunteer goes through a period of frustration and disappointment. At this time, the social worker helps the volunteer to reevaluate the situation and come to terms with a slower rate of progress than may have been anticipated. When this is accomplished, the volunteer exhibits dedication and patience in realistic effort with the patient. In sum, the Case Aide Program appears to have attracted superior and dedicated volunteers who give much and receive much in the process.

THE CASE AIDE SUPERVISOR

One goal of the program has been to make effective use of the limited resource of experienced mental health workers. Considerable care was taken to recruit and screen supervisors. We have found that the Case Aide Program arouses interest among social workers. It offers a new and interesting function and an opportunity to work part-time. We have used workers who are employed elsewhere to supervise evening groups but a majority who applied were not otherwise working at their profession. Available to us were young married women, retired social workers, and some experienced social workers in a doctoral program. While such workers are available, considerable effort is required to locate them and to determine whether they can work successfully in this setting.

Our experience indicates that the program is accomplishing its goal of extending scarce professional manpower. We utilize professional talent that would otherwise lie fallow. Secondly, by using volunteers to work directly with patients and using professional time for supervision, we can triple the number of patients receiving individual attention. Naturally, since volunteers cannot do precisely what a trained professional person does even under supervision, we cannot say that the therapeutic effectiveness is thereby tripled.

Nonetheless, in terms of patients, receiving individual attention, this therapeutic stratagem does increase the effective use of social work time. Our experience has made it quite clear that functioning as a case aide supervisor is essentially a new role for the social worker. The social worker who has a routine attitude does not perform effectively in this setting. There must be enthusiasm for new ventures and a degree of flexibility in defining one's professional role.

To guide volunteers, the worker must use his professional competence in creative ways. He must exercise judgement of the needs and strengths of both patients and volunteers. Since the volunteer is the primary therapeutic agent, the social worker must skillfully guide this process at one remove. The worker must also be able to adjust to a variety of tasks, e.g., recruitment of volunteers, which are not part of his traditional role. No one professional style seems superior to another if the worker has the qualities that give him enthusiasm, flexibility and versatility in handling diverse functions.

Volunteers meet in a group with the worker after seeing their patients. This meeting is very effective for airing and resolving problems under the guidance of a supervisor and with support of a group. Additionally, each volunteer has individual sessions with the supervisor for further guidance and advice of a technical or legal nature. Regular meetings of the supervisors with the senior social worker and the program coordinator are held in which procedures for resolving problems and implementing the program are developed. A core of workers trained in this kind of therapeutic program has now been built up and these methods can be passed to other programs which will develop.

One of the project's goals was to demonstrate that this program could be introduced in other settings. Two mental health associations in Massachusetts, Mystic Valley and Central Middlesex, have been successful in applying our experience. (See Chapter 7.)

The service and demonstration aspects of this program are primary but a research component has been built into our work. Research is being carried out in three areas: the characteristics and reactions of the volunteers; their effect upon patients; and the relation of the program to the community. It is expected that analysis of the data we are collecting will provide both theoretical and very practical information on the functioning of a case aide program.

PLANS FOR THE FUTURE

Progress to date indicates that there is a real need for this service, and that it repays the community both in economic return and particularly in human values.

We believe that we have only begun to exploit the potential of this therapeutic stratagem. Up to this point, we have concentrated on an effort to help chronic patients. We have now begun to explore several other ways of using volunteers together with trained professional staff.

For example, volunteers may be of great value in work with postadolescent psychotics. Student case aides, who are functioning at a very high level, will, we expect, be of unique value in helping their less fortunate older contemporaries. They will be able to relate to these disturbed young people as friends and peers. We believe that there may be unexplored therapeutic gain in this kind of relationship. For young patients who improve in the hospital but have difficulty in the community, the volunteer can offer a service very difficult for the hospital to provide. He can give support and help in the community setting and assist the patient in maintaining himself outside the hospital.

We feel that older case aide volunteers may be able to provide mature, stable support that has been lacking for many mentally ill young adults. For selected cases, we propose to try a team approach with both a student and a mature volunteer working with one patient. The use of case aide volunteers in this specialized manner holds considerable promise.

We plan to begin assigning some of our experienced volunteers to work with selected patients who have been in the hospital for a relatively short period of time but who are not responding to treatment and are in danger of becoming chronic. This assistance to hospital staff would represent a considerable saving in professional man hours and may reduce the chronic population of the hospital.

During these first two years of operation we have noticed a rapid development of skill, sensitivity and leadership qualities among certain volunteers. For example, one volunteer has become an effective discussion leader with a group of patients in our industrial program. For such volunteers, we have initiated an advanced training program. By assuming more professional responsibilities, these skilled volunteers will permit the program to become more economically self-sustaining.

Other advanced volunteers are working in the hospital's home treatment program, helping with transition from halfway houses to the community and working on job placement with patients in the drug addiction unit.

Another important development is the use of group work techniques. In order to reach a greater number of patients, volunteers will be trained to work with patients as a ward group. The reactivation of an entire ward is, in our opinion, a function for the volunteer which must be explored. By use of such a group aide, we hope to enlist the patients themselves in helping each other. We feel that this is a logical extension of the work we are already doing.

In summary, it appears that volunteers and professional persons can develop an effective working partnership for exploring creative ways to attack persisting problems.

Chapter 7

A MENTAL HEALTH ASSOCIATION CASE AIDE PROGRAM AT A LARGE STATE HOSPITAL

DORIS WRIGHT EPSTEIN, M.S.W.*

I N LONG CORRIDORS lined with chairs, seated women stare vacantly into space or out the window, seemingly unaware of each other's existence. The hospital halls are orderly but museum-like: the exhibits are human beings. A visitor is overwhelmed with the feeling of wasted life.

This was a ward of the continued treatment group at Metropolitan State Hospital in Waltham, Massachusetts, in early 1964. Wards were open for the most part, buildings in good repair, personnel dedicated but inadequate in number for these chronically ill women. Even patients with symptoms in remission had little opportunity to return to the community, primarily because of insufficient staff to assist them. No one was available with whom they could form relationships in order to examine problems of their real worlds.

Use of nonprofessional persons, such as college students, to develop relationships with patients has many times been successfully demonstrated. Training of community volunteers for this purpose is now underway in a number of pilot projects. Several members of the Mystic Valley Mental Health Association in Lexington, Massachusetts, and the Mental Health Association of Central Middlesex in Concord, Massachusetts, participated in the Boston State Hospital program and observed its benefits. (See Chapter 6.)

Their experience suggested that a similar program might be

*Supervisor
Mental Health Case Aide Program at the Metropolitan State Hospital
Mystic Valley Mental Health Association
22 Muzzey Street
Lexington, Mass.

sponsored by local associations to serve their regional mental hospital, Metropolitan State Hospital. Student groups had worked there for ten years or so, some in case aide programs,[1] but no mature volunteers had been involved in a carefully supervised arrangement. As pointed out by Mrs. Edward Rolfe, a member of the association committee responsible for this project:

> There was always a small core of volunteers whose interest lay in having close contact with patients; they sought a clearly directed program with specific goals. Their interest could not be developed without professional guidance and supervision, and this was not available from a hard-pressed staff . . . The missing factor was always that of supervision.

In addition to benefits which might be derived by patients, the association members believed that, through experiences of the case aides, the community might increase in understanding of mental illness. Furthermore, a relationship of mutual assistance might be established between the hospital and the rest of the community.

Late in 1964, the two mental health associations of Central Middlesex and Mystic Valley, representing nine towns, began discussions with the hospital's superintendent. They did not attempt to impose a preconceived plan upon the hospital: they asked the administration in what way mental health associations could help the hospital most. As a result of this exploration, the associations proposed to sponsor a case aide program for which they would provide funds for supervision and active community liaison. The hospital administration accepted with gratitude and assured their full cooperation.

From the beginning, the committee believed that volunteers should be selected carefully and supervised by a social worker. The project would attempt to help patients reach the point of leaving the hospital and would assist in their adjustment to community living. All planning was focused on the best solutions for individual patients, based on sound understanding of their needs as human beings.

During the first month after her selection, the supervising social

---

[1] Umbarger, C.C., Dalsimer, J.S., Morrison, A.P., and Breggin, P.R.: *College Students in a Mental Hospital.* New York, Grune & Stratton, 1962.

worker surveyed the literature but little could be found in professional journals about similar programs. Consultation with persons from other agencies was more fruitful. This eliminated potential pitfalls and gave direction to the program. All ideas were
discussed thoroughly with the committee representing the two
associations.

Learning about the hospital, its history and method of functioning, as well as meeting key personnel was accomplished through
the generous cooperation of the director of social service. From the
same source came suggestions of appropriate patients. Records
were read by the social worker, patients interviewed, and those who
might respond to help were selected. Criteria were mainly the
patient's ability to relate to a case aide and a prognosis indicating
that with assistance the patient might be expected to leave the
hospital within a year.

Recruitment of case aides came next. With individual invitations
to key people in two communities and releases in local papers, two
coffee hours were arranged for prospective participants. The program was explained by the social worker and enlivened by personal accounts of case aide work at Boston State Hospital.

Forces of natural selection seemed to yield people appropriate
for the program. Those with interest, sincerity, warmth, empathy,
intelligence and understanding joined; those who were uncertain
needed little help in withdrawing. Thirteen case aides, a patient
for each, and the social worker were ready to begin at the end of
a month.

The original commitment of each case aide was one half-day a
week for a year. Flexibility is necessary, particularly during the
summer, but absences are planned with the patients and contact is
continued by correspondence. As patients move to the community,
case aides are expected to maintain a relationship within limits of
time and geography.

The case aides met their patients during their first trip to the
hospital. They would continue to spend one morning a week with
them for the next year. Part of the morning would be spent with
the patient, part in individual conference with the social worker,
and the remainder of the time in group meeting.

Group meetings are intended to increase the case aides' understanding of mental illness and to improve techniques utilized in a therapeutic relationship. Topics presented have included interviewing, mental hospital administration, treatment of psychotics, and reports from the literature on research. Sometimes presentations are made by outside experts, at other times by the social worker.

Further supervision is provided by a monthly half-hour conference between each case aide and the social worker, and by any other consultation deemed necessary. Advancement for the case aide lies in assuming responsibility for working with more complicated problems as her ability increases.

In assessing the program to date, two things stand out: patients involved are being helped; case aides learn a great deal about mental illness, about helping patients, and about themselves.

The thirteen patients are all women, aged from thirty-nine to eighty-three, who have been hospitalized between three and thirty years. Most are schizophrenic, all are considered chronically ill and all have had the maximum treatment available at the hospital. Most of the patients either have no families or have a disturbing situation at home.

Initially, these patients were merely passively cooperative with their case aides, the exception being one who announced immediately that she had no use for a visitor. This was a shock, to say the least, on the beginning day. The inexperienced young case aide said to the social worker, "I'll see what I can do if you will leave us alone." She began immediately to form a solidly-based relationship.

Progress in this situation has been almost dramatic. At first the patient only sat in the ward as she had been doing for years, always in the same chair, appearance messy, activity lacking. She began to respond by wearing a clean dress, talking a little, eventually walking to the door, then leaving the building, but only to please her case aide. Now she rides to a nearby restaurant for snacks and is concerned about what others think of her appearance. Throughout, she has been encouraged by the case aide's friendly interest to talk about matters that worried her: divorce and custody action taken by her husband, or visits by faultfinding relatives. All this was accomplished by a spontaneous and dedicated woman whose inexperience was little hindrance to her effectiveness in a supervised setting.

A withdrawn widow who responded minimally, often reverting to delusional material, was first encouraged to engage in limited and superficial socializing with case aides and other patients. A turning point seemed to come when the case aide was able to inquire comfortably about the patient's deceased husband. With obvious sympathetic understanding, she helped her patient to share memories of a most satisfying marriage and to maintain focus on reality instead of fantasy.

The most elderly patients in the group are thought of affectionately as elderly relatives to whom age has brought limitations. By coincidence, one who emigrated from Sweden has a Swedish case aide. Through common language they established an immediate bond which has continued to grow in depth.

As resocialization of patients progressed, the huge problem loomed of community placement. Nursing homes seemed inappropriate for physically well patients. Most had no family home to which to return, and they would be unable to live independent isolated lives outside the hospital. *Family care* seemed the logical solution, but it was not in effect at this hospital.

Family care is a program authorized by the Department of Mental Health in which patients still under the hospital's care are placed in private homes approved by hospital staff. The state pays the family a modest allowance for board and room, and continues its responsibility for providing medical and casework supervision, medicines and clothing. Because of personnel shortages, Metropolitan State had not been able to make use of this program.

Again the associations carefully weighed the issue and began a discussion with hospital administration. *Family care* was agreed upon, but the associations would have to use their resources in locating homes. These arrangements have been satisfactorily accomplished. The hospital assumes responsibility for approving homes and, since patients remain on hospital census, it retains responsibility for the patient's physical needs. Supervision of patients in the home will be provided by the associations until a larger professional staff may permit the hospital to assume this duty.

Responsibility for finding homes was taken by association volunteers. They canvassed key members of their communities to publicize the need. They arranged for excellent newspaper features which stimulated families to offer homes. Helping the first patient to leave the hospital for *family care* foster home has meant the accomplishment of a major goal. The thrill of this first placement was shared by the whole group. Other patients will soon follow now that homes have been found.

Reinvolving discouraged relatives has helped patients, too. For some families, the possibility of a *family care* arrangement means that they can show interest without fear that they will be forced to have the patient live with them. Patients then become aware that they are not completely isolated. Sometimes a renewed family relationship results in material gain, new eyeglasses or a hearing aid, to bring the world closer.

The case aides' satisfaction from their learning experience has been an extra dividend. The first group consists of dedicated housewives from twenty-five to fifty years old with levels of education varying from high school to graduate school. Most are simply interested in helping someone. If they had been chosen only for their perceptiveness, other qualities might have been missed such as warmth, spontaneity or intelligence. As it is, there is a wide range of abilities. This is evident in their conception of problems and in their capacity for growth. Some emphasize development of a relationship with the patient; others emphasize creating changes in the external environment.

Many are keen to learn in an educational process and enjoy putting to use newly acquired knowledge. Some of these women may go on to further mental health training.

By the end of four months, all case aides had completed a detailed study of their patients based on their understanding and experience up to that time. They said that while this was a difficult task they enjoyed having to think about details of their work. As a result of these studies, the case aides were able to set more objective goals for their patients. Furthermore, with goals which they themselves had set, the aides were able to derive greater satisfaction from their work.

Increasing community understanding of mental illness, a major goal of the project, can be observed. The case aides have learned, disseminated their knowledge, and shared their concern with friends and associates. Other volunteers have become involved in publicity, recruiting, home-finding, and in maintenance of comprehensive records.

"From its early days," stated Mrs. Rolfe of the association committee, "the program was seen as a vehicle for communication between the state institution and the area it serves . . . There was even a vision of interested citizens becoming a force to support mental health legislation and improved local resources . . . The hospital staff could see this program as the community's sharing responsibility for human beings it had long neglected."

Hospital personnel, from ward attendants to professional workers, have commended the project and say that it is achieving the goals it set out to accomplish.

As patients are moved out of the hospital and community resources are mobilized to further their adjustment, the program will continue with other patients. When the time arrives to incorporate this program in the hospital's functioning, the flow of communication between hospital and community will be a factor in truly community-based aftercare services.

Chapter 8

THE VISTA VOLUNTEER PROGRAM AT THE BOSTON STATE HOSPITAL

ERNEST A. KRAUS, M.S.W.*

INTRODUCTION

In accordance with the President's Economic Opportunity Act, Boston State Hospital requested twelve VISTA[1] workers, Volunteers in Service to America. These idealistic young people, actually members of a domestic peace corps, were assigned full time to the hospital for a period of twelve months.

Boston State Hospital's unique demonstration and research experience with volunteers was the basis for this program. Its goals emphasize reintegration into society of individuals who have failed assimilation because of long-standing social and emotional deficits. By giving VISTA Volunteers an opportunity to provide services to a wide variety of patients, it was hoped that many new and creative uses for volunteers would be defined and demonstrated.

THE SETTING AT BOSTON STATE HOSPITAL

Boston State Hospital, the largest hospital for the mentally ill in Massachusetts, draws its patient population from the City of Boston. Within this city live a substantial number of low-income, multiproblem families and large racially and ethnically segregated minority groups. The hospital's neighborhood is under-

*Formerly, VISTA Coordinator
Boston State Hospital
591 Morton Street
Boston, Mass.

[1] The VISTA Executive Committee includes the following: Milton Greenblatt, M.D., Superintendent, Boston State Hospital; Arnold Abrams, M.D., Assistant Superintendent, Boston State Hospital; Maida H. Solomon, B.A., B.S., Consultant in Psychiatric Social Work and Social Psychiatry; Victor A. Gelineau, Ph.D., Consultant in Research; David Kantor, Ph.D., Consultant in Community Psychiatry; John H. Brennan, M.D., Chief of Male Continued Treatment Service.

going rapid social change as it absorbs an influx of low income and deprived families.

This hospital with a patient population of one thousand nine hundred and an annual intake of two thousand patients is supervised by the Department of Mental Health and affiliated with a large number of training and educational institutions. It carries out a heavy schedule of undergraduate and graduate teaching in psychiatry for Tufts and Boston University Medical Schools. Nursing affiliations are arranged for Boston City, St. Elizabeth's, and Beverly Hospitals. Graduate students from Boston University and Simmons College School of Social Work are offered training in social work; some training in psychology is available to students of Boston University and Harvard University. Other universities are also affiliated with the hospital.

The hospital has its own large geriatric service and recently added an adolescent service, a drug addiction unit, and a halfway house. Increasingly, the hospital is developing into a community psychiatric setting.

PREPARATION FOR VISTA VOLUNTEERS

It was reasoned that in an institution as large as Boston State Hospital having many diverse programs each with its own history, objectives, and operational procedures, it was the responsibility of the sponsoring institution to work out an intelligent plan of orientation for the volunteers. The hospital's VISTA Executive Committee created the position of coordinator, or overall supervisor, in order to interpret the objectives of the VISTA Program to hospital staff (professional and otherwise) and to mobilize professional staff to employ and supervise volunteers on their services.

The Executive Committee believed that one person should be responsible for the administration and supervision of a program in which twelve young, inexperienced individuals would work full-time on many different projects involving many professional disciplines and various levels of supervisory experience. The coordinator was to be responsible for knowing where the volunteers were employed, what they were doing, and how much time they were spending. He would maintain communication with supervisors and good working arrangements.

Before the volunteers arrived, the coordinator prepared a short, descriptive account of the important and interesting services at the hospital. This together with a tour of the hospital and a discussion of its history made up the basic plan for orientation. The VISTA volunteers were permitted choice of assignments with the understanding that their choice be in accordance with the hospital's needs for service.

The VISTA Volunteers reached the hospital in two groups, one of four and one of eight persons. The first group came in May. They had received six weeks' preliminary training at the University of Maryland School of Social Work, Baltimore. The second group arrived early in August. Their training site was the Mary McDonald Settlement House in Chicago, Illinois. These training programs were under the auspices of the federal government. The hospital's plans for orientation proved successful and at this writing the VISTA volunteers are employed on fourteen distinct hospital projects.

PROJECT ASSIGNMENT PROPOSALS

Several specific assignments were proposed for the VISTA Volunteers. During the first few months, the following programs have been established.

Service to Patients as Social Work Assistants

Through their choice of placements, several VISTA Volunteers are functioning as social work aides in the screening unit as well as in the home treatment service, the women's continued treatment services, the new adolescent unit, and the geriatric service.

In the screening unit, two VISTA Volunteers talk with new patients and take family and medical histories. Their assignments in home treatment include relieving a mother of her household and child-care duties once a week so that she can go shopping and move about in the community; acting as a friendly visitor with another woman patient, and working with the children in a third family to try to introduce new thought and behavior patterns in handling family crises.

In the women's continued treatment service, the VISTA Volunteer assists with several patients through "friendship therapy" as do several volunteers in the adolescent unit. One VISTA Volunteer works with geriatric patients on a one-to-one basis. She initiated a nursing home candidates' discussion group and does follow-ups on discharged patients.

Cooperation with New Programs and Projects

VISTA Volunteers have taken a large responsibility in advancing the hospital's new programs. Four of them are assigned to the adolescent unit. They function in several capacities. As recreational aides they conduct ballroom and folk dances, plan parties around patriotic holiday themes and accompany adolescents off the grounds to recreational facilities.

They work as tutors with patients who attend school off the grounds, assisting with reading, math and even Latin. They act as a serious friend who has time to listen, encouraging adolescents to develop their positive strengths.

Two VISTAS are involved in a nursing home study project. Their assignment includes friendly visiting, observation and recording of researchable information; interpreting to nursing home staff the objectives of the project and sharing information on the patients. They help motivate nursing home staff to develop activities such as games, singing, and simple arts and crafts to encourage interpersonal relationships among the patients in the home.

One VISTA has selected the drug unit for an assignment. He spends his time talking with patients, accompanying them to functions on the grounds and conducting a music listening group. Another VISTA spends his evenings with the patients in a new coeducational unit of eight working patients, acting as a friendly visitor and group leader.

Three VISTAS work in a day hospital with patients of both sexes, mixed diagnoses, and a wide age span. Although this day hospital is not new, some of the programs introduced by the VISTAS are. These include art appreciation and visiting former patient friends who now reside in nursing homes. One VISTA is involved in the ever-expanding hospital industries program. She is responsible for part of the operation of the hospital's employment office.

Contact with Other Agencies

One VISTA Volunteer through his assignment with family care

learned of the roles of the Visiting Nurse Association, the Department of Welfare, and the hospital's nursing school affiliates. Other VISTAS associated with the nursing home study project and geriatrics are visiting in eight nursing homes. Still others in the screening unit are beginning to know the roles of several community agencies such as the Department of Welfare and the Boston City Hospital. Several VISTAS working with adolescents in the drug addiction unit have come in contact with employment agencies and know firsthand the school problems of our young patients.

Establishment of New Roles for Volunteers Working with the Chronically Ill and Severely Retarded

Several VISTAS work with chronic patients. One VISTA started a library in the women's continued treatment service. A group of patients under her direction have published one edition of a building magazine. Another VISTA works in the men's continued treatment service with several regressed men and has established sufficient rapport that these patients are willing to go off the grounds on fishing trips and to the movies. Several VISTAS work in the night hospital in a new rehabilitation program with regressed patients who have had a minimum of interpersonal relationships.

TRAINING FOR KNOWLEDGEABLE PERFORMANCE

The VISTA Volunteers are guided in their work placements by psychiatrists, social workers, nurses and other professional staff. Volunteers have the opportunity to learn about the treatment of mental illness and the resources and agencies currently involved. The goal of their supervision is to point out and clarify problems which arise during their work in an ongoing mental institution. The underlying principle of all supervision is to maximize the volunteer's potential for creativity, imagination and initiative and to help him understand how to use his natural abilities and personal resources in his work with patients.

The VISTA Volunteers through formal lectures available to the entire hospital staff make use of the hospital's rich teaching activities. The ideas heard at these sessions are discussed among the VISTAS themselves and with the coordinator.

Each of the services employing VISTA Volunteers conducts a weekly conference for all persons in the service. Through these group conferences, the volunteers participate with other staff in open discussion of the problems and issues to be resolved within the service. They are thus able to make a contribution and hear their ideas evaluated.

Through assigned supervisors from their services, the VISTA Volunteers receive scheduled weekly individual and group supervision where the content focuses on the patient and his problems, the meaning of his behavior, the forces at work in his life, and practical plans for motivating him to begin to use his positive strengths.

Of the total time spent in supervision, approximately 70 per cent is given in groups and 30 per cent, individually. There is some variation according to the preference of the professional supervisor.

The VISTA Volunteers meet weekly with a psychiatrist. A statement of his objectives follows:

> It was initially decided that it might be helpful to the VISTA Volunteers to get together as a group with a psychiatrist as a leader. There was no particular format envisaged and the agenda was left quite open. However, it has clearly evolved that this meeting has become a weekly group therapy session and in my opinion it is of extreme value and I would strongly recommend that this be written into all future volunteer programs and, in fact, I feel that it is almost essential that there be such a session for this group. I intend to continue these meetings weekly for an hour and a half while this group is in this hospital.[1]

The VISTA Volunteers also meet weekly with the coordinator in a seminar. The content of the seminar is administrative as well as educational, including free discussion on issues facing the VISTAS and review of interesting comments from their brief weekly records. A different VISTA reports on his work every other week. On the alternate weeks, guests selected by the VISTAS are invited to discuss their work and answer questions. These guests can be persons from outside the hospital community. The coordinator is also available for individual consultation.

---

[1] The group's leader has been N. Michael Murphy, M.D.

Following are some comments culled from reports of five VISTA Volunteers. They are included here to illustrate the VISTAS' work, their frustrations and their sincere effort to understand their experiences.

> My work, as I perceive it, now consists, in part, of giving myself daily tasks which challenge me but do not overwhelm me—tasks which allow me to practice my particular skills and where the expectations surrounding me are not frightening.
>
> Individual attention is the most urgent need of the patients. We try to give each one something. . . . This is the thing that proves most frustrating to me. I have also found that as relationships become more intimate, more problems arise in how to deal with the patients. . . . As difficulties arise and the lack of experience becomes all too evident, I tend to become discouraged.
>
> No one knows the patient I ask about . . . no one expects this patient to get well . . . She wants direction, but the doctor tells me to accept her reality.
>
> I took a patient home. All the way home the patient acted very well. She really did not need anyone to go with her. However, when we got to her home her whole attitude and personality changed. While together she talked softly and acted properly, but when she was talking to her daughter and son-in-law she talked very loud, repeated herself constantly and had a nervous twitching of the whole body. This was the first patient's home I visited. I think I was made more aware of how important a factor the home environment is in contributing to good mental health.
>
> One of the patients with whom I have been working quite intensively finally felt confident enough to actually talk with me about a problem that he never talked about freely with anyone. This particular experience gave me a little sense of accomplishment for a couple of reasons: (1) the doctor felt that it would be sort of a waste of time to work with this patient, (2) the patient for the last two weeks had responded very negatively to me and I thought that I was not even getting through to him. I feel this patient has made a small step in the right direction which may lead to his discharge . . .

The problem of what to do, how to do, when to do, and when not to do are all mirrored here. The VISTA Volunteers are not "keepers of the keys." They seek to understand and involve themselves in the lives and dilemmas of the patients with whom they work. They want to "reach" the patients, to know the personal problems which arise from their sickness and from the hospital routines, and they want to bring "justice" into their lives.

CONCLUSION

The VISTA Volunteer project at the Boston State Hospital can be described as always challenging, often enlightening, sometimes trying, and always rewarding for the VISTA Executive Committee, the cooperating hospital personnel, the coordinator, and the VISTA Volunteers.

Although this is the account of only six months' experience, we believe that it gives further evidence of new horizons for volunteers in a state mental hospital. It has again been demonstrated that when volunteers are carefully oriented to the hospital's problems and objectives, when they are carefully supervised, when they are given an opportunity to participate with other staff, their work need not be limited to parties, games, and simple clerical tasks. The morale of the volunteer is better, his dedication more permanent and he becomes able to take his place alongside staff as an important adjunct to their work.

Although asked to work only forty-five hours a week, the VISTA Volunteers' average contribution of time is closer to fifty-five hours.

The professionals and total hospital staff who work with these young people value their contribution to the everyday efforts that count in the lives of the patients.

It was said by Walt Whitman, "Behold, I do not give lectures or a little charity, when I give myself." This is true of VISTA Volunteers.

Chapter 9

"FASHION THERAPY"
DIARY OF A REHABILITATION TECHNIQUE FOR CHRONIC FEMALE PATIENTS

ELIZABETH MARY REMAR*

INTRODUCTION

ALL WOMEN desire to be attractive: the fashion therapy course is predicated upon this premise. By attention to individual appearance, the course attempts to renew self-respect and confidence so often lost among long-hospitalized persons. Once the basic techniques of make-up, hair-dressing, wardrobe planning, and poise have been acquired, it is hoped that the patient will continue to enhance her appearance as well as other aspects of her personality.

Personal contact with volunteers provides a warm human relationship so important for progress toward mental health. The very presence of the volunteer is a bridge to the outside world. For a volunteer, "fashion therapy" provides common ground on which women can establish rapport.

The Fashion Therapy Pilot Project[1] was conducted under the sponsorship of the Massachusetts Association for Mental Health at Boston State Hospital from October, 1964, to May, 1965. Twenty

*During the project the author was Director of Public Relations, Massachusetts Association for Mental Health. A more detailed report may be obtained by writing to the author at the following address.
Director of Volunteer Services
Boston State Hospital
591 Morton Street
Boston, Mass·

[1] The author wishes to acknowledge the assistance in this project of: Mrs. Mildred Alberts, owner, and Miss Frances Selfo, teacher, *Academie Moderne* charm school, Boston, Mass.; Miss Marie Orlandello, occupational therapist and supervisor of the project; Zayre's department store, Roslindale, Mass.; and the Milton, Mass., chapter of B'nai B'rith, Mrs. Phillip Halpern, President.

women, including ten female patients from chronic wards and ten volunteers, participated together in a good grooming and charm course taught by a professional instructor. The course began with volunteer orientation and concluded with a fashion show by patients. In all, the project consisted of three orientation sessions and twelve one and one-half hour teaching sessions. Although subjects covered were similar to those in an "outside" school, there was special challenge in the necessity for imaginative interpretation of the lessons.

PREPARATION

In October of 1964, a department store assisted by a chapter of B'nai B'rith staged a fashion show for patients at the Boston State Hospital. Following this show, many members of the chapter wished to contribute further through closer contact with patients. The author was aware that state hospitals in California and Maryland[2] had employed "fashion therapy" since 1959, and therefore seized this opportunity to initiate the program in Massachusetts.

With the hospital superintendent's permission, the author sought cooperation of a charm school in Boston. The owner of this school generously provided a good grooming and charm course including the services of a teacher. Local merchants donated cosmetics, clothing, shoes, handbags, hair brushes and many other items.

An occupational therapist was assigned by the hospital to supervise the project, working with the teacher, volunteers, and patients.

Time and day for the teaching sessions were selected by hospital staff so that the majority of patients would be able to attend every session.

SELECTION AND ORIENTATION

The B'nai B'rith volunteers came to the hospital for screening and orientation. Fifteen women were interviewed by the director of volunteer services and the occupational therapist; ten were selected. The single most important qualification seemed to be the volunteer's interest in the project. Other important qualities were a warm, accepting attitude, resourcefulness, and a willingness to go beyond what is required.

---

[2] Projects of the San Francisco Association for Mental Health—Fashion Group of San Francisco, Inc., and the Maryland Association for Mental Health.

Ten female patients from one of the continued treatment buildings were selected by staff on the basis that they were likely to benefit from the course. All patients were schizophrenics who had been hospitalized between two and eleven years. The youngest was in her early twenties and the oldest, sixty-eight. The author feels that a majority of patients selected should be persons who, with reassurance, might be expected to leave the hospital. Inclusion of patients likely to remain in the hospital should not be eliminated, but neither should their number dominate the group.

Prior to the course, it is important for volunteers to meet with hospital personnel. It is helpful to learn from them the patients' background in order to plan a suitable experience. A visit to the building where patients live encourages a realistic approach to the limitations of their environment.

During the week following selection of volunteers, a brief orientation was held to provide information about the hospital and about mental illness. During the next week, volunteers and patients became acquainted at a coffee hour.

PROCEDURE OF THE COURSE

The first teaching session was devoted to posture and simple physical exercises with patients and volunteers participating together. Simple exercises for improved posture and poise were taught.

Throughout the course, teacher and volunteers adopted an attitude of encouragement and gentle steering to a favorable decision. Patients were not arbitrarily told how to dress, wear make-up, or walk. Through practicing all that was demonstrated, patients were able to understand how to make more favorable choices.

At the second session it was observed that some patients had been very faithful and active in doing their "homework." Three had helped patients who did not respond as quickly. By the third teaching session all patients participated.

The third session was devoted to personal hygiene. Complete toilet kits and containers for personal articles were distributed marked with patients' names and individual designs.

At the fourth session it was obvious that four of the patients had made an effort to groom themselves. One of the patients told the author that she had arranged her hair the night before in order to appear "nice for the other ladies."

For the fifth session the ladies went by bus to the charm school for a class in makeup. The occupational therapist had obtained cosmetics suited to the appearance of each person. An air of festivity and excitement was manifest among patients and volunteers.

By the end of the sixth session it was noted that patients who had been too reticent or disinterested to participate in previous sessions were now willing, if not eager, to take part. If allowed to watch the others, reluctant patients became interested. None were made to feel uncomfortable when they decided not to cooperate. Some patients sustained a high level of interest throughout the course; others took some time before actively participating. Others cooperated or not depending on their mood at that particular session.

The seventh and eighth sessions were devoted to hair styling. It was noticed that four patients were thereby encouraged to visit the hospital hairdresser.

When it was announced at the eighth session that the final meeting would be a fashion show, the air of anticipation and excitement was delightful to see. Patients would be the models, wearing outfits which would be given to them. Several patients expressed doubt or fear about the show. They were reassured that the show was intended only for the members' pleasure, that the audience would consist only of the volunteers and certain hospital and association staff whom they knew well. Patients who continued to express fear were told that they need not participate unless they wished. As it turned out, all patients participated, with expressions of enjoyment as they modeled their new outfits.

During the ninth session, items donated for patients' outfits were brought in by a wardrobe committee of three volunteers. The teacher demonstrated how to dress attractively and economically, using patients' new outfits as examples. The volunteer committee took charge of alterations and marking of each article with the patient's name. In this way, volunteers who could not work directly with patients were also able to contribute.

During the closing sessions, preparations were made for the fashion show. An air of calmness and gentle direction should be maintained throughout the course, but *this is particularly impor-*

tant at the rehearsal, and at the final fashion show. Volunteers must realize that standing up in front of an audience in a fashion show is a tremendous step for the patient.

On the morning of "graduation," patients and volunteers traveled together from the hospital to the school. Volunteers assisted patients with their last minute preparations. It was obvious that they felt a sense of pride in the patients who now looked well-groomed and attractively dressed, a long way from their neglected appearance at the beginning of the course.

During the show, a record player provided soft background music which lent a professional and festive air to the occasion. The teacher gave a fashion commentary as each patient modeled. Each one was greeted with soft but warm and spontaneous applause.

At the end of the show, the teacher awarded graduation certificates which were received with many expressions of delight. Patients and volunteers expressed great regret that the course was over; it was obvious that a friendly relationship had developed between them. The volunteers were urged to continue to visit their patients on an informal basis.

SUMMARY

This program was undertaken to ascertain whether a good grooming and charm course could remotivate a group of chronic, long-hospitalized women patients in a state mental hospital. It demonstrated that intensive contact with sympathetic volunteers in a well-constructed program does indeed have a favorable effect.

The author feels that it would be very helpful if an alumnae group could be formed so that volunteers could keep in contact with their patients and encourage them to plan activities of their own. When dealing with patients who have been hospitalized for so long, a continued relationship with the volunteers at the end of the formal course is essential.

Realistic is the key word in any volunteer program. The volunteer must appreciate the patient and her environment at the hospital in order to work constructively *with* the situation, rather than against it.

Chapter 10

A MENTAL HEALTH ASSOCIATION PAID EMPLOYMENT WORKSHOP IN A STATE HOSPITAL

EDNA STEIN*

INTRODUCTION

THE EFFECTIVENESS of *work for pay* as a therapeutic technique has been surprisingly neglected in the rehabilitation of long-hospitalized patients in the United States. In this highly industrialized society which stresses achievement, productivity, and the correlation between monetary returns and personal success, work is not only an economic but also an important social institution.

Yet, workshops are rare in mental hospitals. Although they have existed in prisons and in a few veterans' mental hospitals, to our knowledge, the sheltered workshop[1] at the Metropolitan State Hospital in Waltham, Massachusetts, was the first one of its kind to be successfully functioning in the United States. It is operated for the benefit of mentally ill patients by the Brookline Association for Mental Health, a private nonprofit agency, in a public mental hospital.

HISTORY

In March, 1960, on a tour of the hospital, the author was shocked by the number of patients sitting idly on the wards with

*President
Brookline Association for Mental Health
43 Garrison Road
Brookline, Mass.

[1] The author wishes to acknowledge the assistance of the following persons in this project: William F. McLaughlin, M.D., Superintendent, Metropolitan State Hospital; Mr. John Levis, Chief Mental Disability Supervisor, Massachusetts Rehabilitation Commission; Mr. Michael Stein, engineer, volunteer workshop director.

absolutely nothing to do. They begged for cigarettes, money, and small personal items.

Chronically hospitalized patients come mainly from the poorest classes and they are further impoverished during their stay in the hospital. They have no spending money from families or the state and no means of earning money to buy even little things such as playing cards, cosmetics, combs, or sweets. The results of prolonged inactivity, apathy, passivity and withdrawal, are apparent.

Although some patients in this hospital were involved in hospital industry, and a very limited number in occupational therapy, the majority were involved in no activity whatsoever. None were gainfully employed.

To determine what could be done, the president of the association met with the Massachusetts Commissioner of Mental Health to explore a possible course of action. He was cordial and interested and we agreed that the association would devise a pilot program to be carried out cooperatively with the superintendent of the hospital. An *ad hoc* advisory committee was appointed, with representatives from the Department of Mental Health, the hospital, the Massachusetts Rehabilitation Commission, and labor unions. As chairman of the committee, the president of the association read a great deal about sheltered workshops, observed one at a veterans' hospital, and through arrangements made by the World Federation for Mental Health, she visited mental hospital workshops in England, France, Holland, Italy and the Soviet Union.

The advisory committee met for six months and made the following recommendations: (1) that a sheltered workshop be established, to be licensed by the federal government for the purpose of providing evaluation, training and employment to carefully selected patients; (2) that the Metropolitan State Hospital provide space, utilities, and patients; (3) that the Massachusetts Rehabilitation Commission use the workshop for evaluation and training, for which a fee would be paid to the association for each patient-client, and (4) that the association operate the workshop, solicit and maintain contracts, and be responsible for administration, bookkeeping and staff.

The sheltered workshop was accordingly opened in May, 1961. Its permit grants exemption from taxes, workmen's compensation, and the minimum wage law. While a lower minimum wage is set, we were cautioned to provide fair wages and to compete fairly for markets. The workshop is, in fact, a small business under nonprofit auspices, operating for the rehabilitation of mentally handicapped men and women. It provides remunerative employment in a setting approximating normal industry as closely as possible. It is a bridge to the outside for some, and provides work and money for others who are unlikely to leave the hospital. The kind of work performed is less important than its value to learn or relearn work habits.

The goals of the project are to help patients assume responsibility for behaving in a socially acceptable manner; to help them learn to work with one another; to provide a realistic work experience, teaching skills and work habits in preparation for employment after discharge, and to provide an opportunity to earn money.

Starting in a corner of the occupational therapy shop with one patient, one contract, and one foreman, the workshop has grown steadily. After five months of operation, new and larger quarters were allocated in a separate building. A year later, an adjoining room was added to accommodate the shop's expanding needs. The hospital and the association provide benches, chairs and tools. The contracting companies install machinery necessary for production. Occasionally, the association rents or purchases equipment. The Rehabilitation Commission, through payment of fees for services, provides the funds necessary for the association to operate the workshop.

STAFF

Our constant aim is to demonstrate how much can be done with little money. To get the workshop started, a small grant was obtained.[2] Expenses for staff, administration, equipment and supplies are paid from funds received as fees from the Rehabilitation Commission. All staff members are retired people whose expert skills are secured at salaries far below their acknowledged value. The patients receive *all* the money earned from the contracts.

Contracts for work are the very heart of the project. Advantages to the employer are elimination of indirect labor costs and

[2] This grant was provided by the Permanent Charity Fund, Boston, Massachusetts.

the reduction of overhead. The employer sets the rate of payment in accordance with his own factory production costs. Variety of work is essential: from low to moderately high pressure tasks, from isolated work to group opportunities, from unskilled to semi-skilled operations.

While the needs of patients are paramount, it is necessary to remember that the employer is motivated chiefly by quality, service, and profit. To keep the project successfully operating, reasonable, efficient and predictable levels of production must always be maintained. Balance between patients' needs and the shop's needs is often delicate but most important.

Thirty-two companies have contracted for a total of forty different tasks. Some have been packaging, collating, reclaiming, assembling, sewing, making millinery and shoe trimming, wire bending, wiring and soldering electronic devices, and using simple power machines such as air presses. There have been no accidents, no spoilage, and very few rejects. Employers have been completely satisfied.

The association provides all shop personnel. The workshop director, a volunteer, is the key to the shop's successful operation. He is responsible for overall supervision and finance, checking the daily work and patients' production scheduling, and preparing the weekly payroll. When necessary, he calls on employers, and through his personal contacts, may negotiate new contracts.

The foreman is a full-time employee, who is responsible for the operation of the shop. He assigns work, teaches the techniques, maintains quality control, keeps the daily time and production records of each patient and takes care of all receiving and shipping. It is an advantage that he have some mechanical and factory experience, but more important is his ability to work effectively with patients. Two business agents each work half-time. Their duties are to secure, maintain and develop contracts. They also act as liaison between the foreman and the employers in order to assure all production requirements.

The hospital's social worker for the chronic patient wards is employed during her free time to take care of application forms required by the Rehabilitation Commission for each patient. During her working hours, she is also assigned by the hospital to work with workshop patients. Since she is the only social worker for one thousand, two hundred and fifty chronic patients, this assignment helps to focus her time and skill.

There is no hospital staff member present in the shop during the work day. This fact and the site of its present location set the workshop apart from the hospital emotionally and physically giving it a feeling of the "world outside."

All records, bookkeeping, billings, disbursements, and administration are the responsibility of the association office.

The executive director of the association is peripherally in touch with the entire operation of the workshop. His specific responsibility is supervision of all office administration.

The Rehabilitation Commission has assigned a full time counselor and a part-time psychiatrist to the program. Their major function is evaluation of clients and potential clients. The rehabilitation counselor devotes a great deal of time to vocational planning and job placement. He is the person primarily involved in helping patients to plan for the future. The hospital social worker and the association give some assistance in home-finding and employment opportunities.

In addition to the workshop director, other volunteers have contributed their time in amounts that could never have been paid for. Many skilled people have given consultation, found homes, jobs, and social opportunities for those ready for discharge.

Committee meetings on two levels are held regularly in order to keep this multi-agency arrangement operating efficiently. One committee comprised of agency people working directly with patients meets biweekly to review prospective applicants. They also appraise the behavior and performance of patients already in the workshop to determine appropriate plans for them. There is no fixed time limitation. Termination depends entirely on needs of the individual patient.

Another larger committee comprised of top administrators of all collaborating agencies meets bimonthly. Its function is to keep the lines of communication open, to evaluate the program, to develop administrative policies, and to evolve more effective use of the facility.

PATIENTS EMPLOYED

Although referral of a patient to the workshop must be made

by the ward psychiatrist, he welcomes suggestions by other staff or volunteers. The patient is interviewed by the Rehabilitation Commission's counselor and psychiatrist who decide on his eligibility. There are two groups of patients employed: those who are Rehabilitation Commission clients, and a few who are not. This latter group is accepted at the expense of the association. In some instances, these patients have later become eligible for Rehabilitation Commission services.

On assignment to the shop, the patient receives a sheet outlining the *Conditions of Employment* such as hours of work, coffee breaks, and so on. Compensation is given on a piece-rate basis, the amount varying according to the speed and skill of the individual. A paycheck is deposited weekly to the patient's hospital account. A receipt is given to the patient. Withdrawals can be made according to hospital rules by permission of the ward physician.

Group meetings are held in the workshop so that patients can ask questions, register complaints, discuss leaving the hospital, share ideas about job and home placement, and be apprised of any administrative or work changes.

After four years of operation, the statistics are impressive. A total of one hundred and fifty-three patients, eighty-three women and seventy men have been placed in the workshop. Of this number, one hundred and thirty-one have completed their placement, twenty are still employed in the workshop, and two died of natural causes before completion of their training period. Of the one hundred and thirty-one patients who completed their training, seventy-seven are out of the hospital representing a discharge rate of 59 percent. This compares with 3 percent as the expected normal discharge rate from similar chronic patient populations.

Of the 59 percent of all workers who have been discharged, better than 50 percent are gainfully employed, many for the first time in years. Of the remainder discharged, some are housewives, others are at home with their families, and a few are unaccounted for. It is interesting to note that 63 percent of the men have left and only 54 percent of the women. Of the fifty-four patients still hospitalized, some have been transferred to veterans' hospitals. Many have left for a period of time, but have returned because of recurrence of their illness or failure to make satisfactory adjustment to community living. Many of these patients are now employed in unpaid hospital jobs outside the workshop.

Patients diagnosed as schizophrenic were less likely to complete the workshop experience successfully and return to the community. More closely correlated with outcome, however, was the length of hospitalization regardless of diagnosis. Workshop patients who remained hospitalized had on the average been hospitalized for a much longer period than workshop patients who were discharged.

PROBLEMS

The major problems have centered on securing contracts and patients. Production is so highly mechanized in the United States that it becomes increasingly difficult to find potential operations. Nevertheless, with effort and perseverance it can be done.

Maintaining an adequate flow of patients to maintain the work schedule has presented some difficulty. However, the success of the project has helped to solve this problem. A few outpatients have been accepted successfully and some patients from the admissions unit.

During the first year and a half, wages were paid directly to the patients. Ideally, if there were sufficient staff to counsel on the proper handling of money, this would be the best arrangement. However, patients were spending their money unwisely, lending it to others, or keeping it where it was easily stolen. As a result, no savings were accumulated to provide for expenses after patients were discharged. The arrangement for depositing money was adopted and patients came to agree that this was the better plan.

RESULTS

Success of the sheltered workshop has exceeded all expectations. This project has demonstrated that public and voluntary agencies can collaborate successfully. The hospital has gained a facility that it would otherwise not have. Counselors of the Rehabilitation Commission have been able to use their training and skills effectively in connection with the workshop.

The Brookline Association for Mental Health has gained confidence that it can be a catalyst for new and imaginative experiments. This confidence has already led to the following projects in the community to assist former patients:

1. Two large department stores and one food chain have agreed to hire suitable people who have completed training in the workshop.

2. Two cooperative appartments have been established for discharged workshop patients. (See Chapter 12.)

3. Weekly cooking classes are held for patients nearing the time of discharge.

4. An aftercare program in our town was arranged.

We do not claim completeness for our project, and we do not presume that it is a cure for mental illness. We do believe that work is an experience around which a person in our society builds perhaps the greatest part of his role in life. This sheltered workshop is a demonstration of a most effective means of assisting mentally ill patients to achieve an adequate functioning and negotiating level for return to the community.

Chapter 11

PROP:
A SHELTERED WORKSHOP PROGRAM
SPONSORED BY VOLUNTEERS

NICHOLAS H. THISSE,* ED.M., C.A.G.S.[1]

T HE ABSENCE of structured therapeutic transitional types of vocational training programs for the mentally ill has long been recognized in this country. Understanding administrators, trained personnel, and adequate funds are all necessary and often unavailable. At Boston State Hospital, through recognition of the value of work in the rehabilitation process, PROP, the Patients Rehabilitation Occupational Program, Inc., was initiated on January 13, 1964.[2] Both hospital administration and the business community were instrumental in establishing this program.

PROP is a private, nonprofit sheltered workshop program, licensed by the Department of Labor, which provides patients with paid employment and training in a protective environment without frustrations commonly found in the competitive world of work.

PROP is unique because it is located within the confines of a large state mental institution, and even more important, because it is sponsored by a group of successful businessmen. Because of the knowledge, time and money contributed by these men, PROP

*Coordinator
Patients Rehabilitation Occupational Program, Inc.
Boston State Hospital
591 Morton Street
Boston, Mass.

[1] Certificate of Advanced Graduate Study.

[2] Special acknowledgement is made to Milton Greenblatt, M.D., Superintendent, and Wilmot D. Griffith, M.A., Mental Health Coordinator and Chief of the Rehabilitation Department at Boston State Hospital and to Mr. Theodore T. Schoenfeld, business executive, for the establishment of this program.

73

has grown in twenty short months to become an outstanding vocational rehabilitation program.

MANAGEMENT

A common shortcoming in many workshops is the absence of a strong relationship with the business world. Sheltered workshops share problems familiar to the business world but often lack experienced administrators to deal with these problems. It is for this reason that sponsorship by successful businessmen is significant.

Management of PROP is provided by a thirteen-member board of directors chosen for their personal interest and skills. The board members serve as volunteer consultants. For instance, when legal, financial or production problems arise, they are referred to the appropriate member for resolution. Board members have helped in obtaining PROP work contracts and jobs in the community for PROP workers.

Until recently the monthly board meetings were held in Boston in the evenings. They are now held at the hospital at breakfast time so that board members can have continuing contact with workers and facilities.

All paid employees are hired through the hospital superintendent's office. A trained professional worker was employed as director-consultant to supervise and to coordinate activities of PROP with the hospital's rehabilitation department. Two shop supervisors are paid by the hospital. PROP pays the salaries of a floor lady, an assistant supervisor and a bookkeeper. The board of directors, which raises money and oversees the management of PROP, consists entirely of volunteers. In addition, PROP has two fulltime volunteers who help supervise patients in the various workshops.

WORKERS

Patients are selected for training and employment in the PROP Shops according to two criteria: they must be between the ages of sixteen and sixty; they must be processed by the hospital's rehabilitation department employment office. In the employment office, patients are screened and counseled by vocational rehabilitation counselors to insure maximum effectiveness of the rehabilitation process.

GOALS AND PROCEDURES

Months and even years of concentrated therapeutic effort with a patient may prove fruitless unless the patient is able to return to the world of work and hold a remunerative, productive and satisfying job: thus, the significance of vocational rehabilitation as the primary goal of PROP.

Through employment provided by PROP, patients *build up self-confidence* by observing results of their labor in a finished product. After years of stagnation, often with deep-rooted feelings of rejection and worthlessness, the patient now can relate to something realistic: his place of enployment, his work supervisor, the finished product, and not of least importance, his paycheck.

Patients also learn *good work habits* which are so vitally important in today's competitive labor market. Good work habits consist of getting to work on time, using a time clock, accepting supervision, developing work tolerance and doing one's best on the job.

PROP helps patients to develop *good social habits,* maintaining good personal hygiene, dressing appropriately, and relating to fellow workers.

Interpersonal relationships are increased through daily coffee breaks, a highlight in the PROP shops. Coffee breaks are utilized for discussions oriented toward helping patients become more aware of the realities in life such as finding jobs, using banks, using public recreational facilities, finding a place to live, social security and what it is used for, and many other topics of importance to these patients.

PROP prepares patients for the competitive world of work through its four broad occupational training areas: an *industrial sewing shop* where patients are prepared for competitive employment in garment factories; an *assembly shop* where patients are prepared for competitive employment as assembly-line workers, packers, general factory workers, and related occupations; a *print shop* where patients are prepared for employment as printers and printers' helpers; and a *bookkeeping department* where patients are prepared for employment as bookkeepers, clerks, typists, and general office workers.

Even though privately sponsored, PROP is one of the most important divisions of the rehabilitation department at Boston State

Hospital. The rehabilitation department provides professional services such as vocational counseling, psychological testing, job placement and follow-up, all important in the rehabilitation process.

RESULTS

The status of one hundred and seventy-six patients who have been involved in the activities of PROP from January 13, 1964, to October 1, 1965, is as follows:

Currently employed in PROP Shops	75
Working and living outside hospital	12
Working outside, living in hospital	10
Living outside, not working	4
Living in family care home	7
Working in another hospital work area	26
Living in hospital, not working because of recurring mental or physical illness	30
Transferred to another hospital	2
Living outside, work status unknown	8
Status unknown	2
TOTAL	176

These figures may be unimpressive to persons unfamiliar with mental illness. However, when one realizes that a majority of these patients have been hospitalized for many years, some as long as twenty or thirty, and that many have had little or no work experience, then these figures acquire significance.

The organization and implementation of PROP has taken many long, hard hours of work by many people. Problems have been common. Nevertheless, with support of the Department of Mental Health and the hospital superintendent, PROP has survived and hopefully will continue to overcome each problem as it arises.

Part III

COMMUNITY PROGRAMS FOR FORMER PATIENTS

Chapter 12

THE COOPERATIVE APARTMENT: A MENTAL-HEALTH-ASSOCIATION-SPONSORED RESIDENCE FOR RETURNING PATIENTS

EDNA STEIN*

ELIZABETH HODGMAN, A.C.S.W.†

INTRODUCTION

T HE SUCCESSFUL RETURN of a patient from a mental hospital to community living involves many factors: psychiatric condition, follow-up care, family relationships, vocational capacity, and community resources. Community planning is often essential to provide for a patient's maximum recovery. This chapter will discuss a project sponsored by a voluntary mental health association in cooperation with mental health specialists: a cooperative apartment.[1]

HISTORY

The Brookline Association for Mental Health, a chapter of the Massachusetts Association, was established in 1958, with special interests in hospital volunteer activities and in facilitating the return of patients to the community.

*See Chapter 10, page 65 for Edna Stein's address.

†Psychiatric Social Worker
Brookline Mental Health Clinic
43 Garrison Road
Brookline, Mass.

[1] The authors wish to acknowledge assistance in this project of the following persons: Herbert J. Hoffman, Ph.D., Executive Director, Brookline Association for Mental Health; Mr. John Levis, Chief Mental Disability Supervisor, Massachusetts Rehabilitation Commission; William F. McLaughlin, M.D., Superintendent, Metropolitan State Hospital; Gladys Whipple, M.D., Director, Brookline Mental Health Clinic.

In 1961, the association organized a sheltered workshop in the hospital in order to provide a rehabilitative experience for chronically ill patients.[2] Experience with this project demonstrated the need to provide suitable living quarters for patients who were otherwise ready to leave the hospital. For many patients, the isolation of an inexpensive rented room or the unhealthy environment of disturbed family relationships might contribute to relapse and return to the hospital.

Experience in other communities has shown that some sort of supervised living situation enhances the recovery of certain former patients.[3,4] The Brookline Association, therefore, conferred over a period of several months with hospital and Rehabilitation Commission staff and with professional staff of the Brookline Mental Health Center. They explored the responsibilities required of each group to establish a successful cooperative apartment.

In the plan that evolved, the association would make available a fully furnished apartment to accommodate four women and would assume all housekeeping responsibilities: rent, utilities, insurance, and maintenance. Volunteers would be available to the women in the apartment. A social worker from the Brookline clinic staff would be available to apartment residents, would hold at least one weekly group meeting in the apartment, and in general, coordinate supervision of the occupants. Ultimate medical responsibility would remain with the hospital, as it would with any other discharged patients. The Massachusetts Rehabilitation Commission counselor would provide vocational counseling, further training and placement as indicated.

THE SEARCH FOR A SITE

Finding a suitable apartment was not easy. The landlord had to

---

[2] Hoffman, H.J.: Paid employment as a rehabilitative technique in a state mental hospital: a demonstration. *Ment Hyg, 49*:193-207, 1965. (This project is reported in Chapter 10.)

[3] Beard, J.H.. Smith, M.M., and Sorokin, F.: An apartment program for post-hospitalized psychiatric patients, in Grob, S., ed.: *The Community Social Club and the Returning Mental Patient.* National Institute of Mental Health. Proceedings of a Conference, Framingham, Mass., 1963. (Available from Center Club, 48 Boylston St., Boston, Mass.)

[4] Sharp, G.A.: A perspective on the function of the psychiatric halfway house. *Ment Hyg, 48*:552-557, 1964.

be willing to have former mental patients as tenants and to accept the fact that there would be a changing group of residents. To counter his reluctance, the association assumed responsibility for holding the lease, for paying the rent, and for behavior of all residents in the apartment. Many advertisements were answered, many contracts made, but individual landlords were fearful of the imagined risk involved. No amount of assurance could sway them. Therefore, an apartment was leased from a management company to whom only minimal information about the residents was given. The one extra clause inserted into the lease allowed the owner to terminate the agreement upon thirty days notice.

For the association, the experience was important in reassessing attitudes toward the mentally ill, and the scope of educational work still to be done. The apartment program has received modest amounts of publicity in the community, but the exact location and telephone number of the apartment is considered confidential information in order to protect the residents from possible harassment and prejudice.

DESCRIPTION OF SETTING

In October, 1963, the cooperative apartment was opened in Brookline to accommodate four women who had been discharged from the Metropolitan State Hospital. A large, two-bedroom apartment was found in a good lower-middle-class apartment house neighborhood, convenient to stores, transportation, service, and amusement facilities. It was attractively furnished by association volunteers. Second-hand furniture was secured from individuals and a local hotel. Complete household linens were supplied by a charitable organization. New bedding, kitchenware, and appliances were purchased. Some food supplies were provided. Funds for all necessary expenditures were obtained from donations by individuals.

The association pays all actual bills: rent, gas, electricity, telephone, maintenance, and occasional cleaning service. Each resident pays ten dollars a week to the association for rent and facilities. This fee was established in accordance with actual cost of operating the apartment. All record keeping and payment of bills is done through the office of the association.

MANAGEMENT OF THE APARTMENT

The residents are responsible for maintenance of the apartment and for buying and cooking their own food. Arrangements have varied with the groups in residence. At times, they have pooled their money and have lived "family style"; at times, they have shopped and prepared their meals individually. There are very few rules. The major guideline has been consideration of the rights and privileges of other residents. Visiting has been limited to 11:00 P.M. on weeknights with no specific curfew for weekends. Female friends and children may stay overnight if agreeable to the apartment members. Meals eaten by guests are paid for at a set rate. Alcoholic beverages are permitted in moderation provided their use does not affect a resident's emotional or medical problem. Although the rules are not always strictly observed, they do provide guidelines.

CRITERIA FOR PATIENT SELECTION

Patients may be accepted for the apartment who have achieved maximum benefit from their hospitalization, who appear to be ready for unsupervised semi-independent community living, who have shown some ability to work, and who have no families or other ties supportive to the adjustment process. Since Brookline is affiliated with the Metropolitan State Hospital, patients from that hospital have priority, and patients who have participated in the sheltered workshop are given further preference because of the previous investment in them.

If such patients are not available, women from other facilities in the Boston area are considered. In order to assess its suitability for themselves, all patients have an opportunity to visit the apartment and meet the current apartment residents. Some patients choose to spend a weekend there in order to evaluate it further.

AGENCY RESPONSIBILITY

The apartment project is a cooperative venture in the sense that many agencies collaborate to formulate and implement a rehabilitation plan and to provide the essential psychiatric follow-up care.

The Apartment Meeting

On a semimonthly basis, the hospital social worker, the Rehabilitation Commission counselor, some volunteers and the executive director of the association, and the psychiatric social worker of the Brookline Mental Health Center meet to consider apartment applicants. Although the hospital psychiatrist is not present at these meetings, his evaluation of a patient's suitability for the apartment is presented by the hospital social worker. If an applicant is considered acceptable by this group, she is seen by the clinic psychiatric social worker; she also visits the apartment. Then the patient and the staff make their decision.

Another purpose of these meetings is to provide an opportunity for agency representatives to discuss the adjustment of those already in residence. Decisions are made about each individual's termination of apartment residency and plans are made for her independent living. Each agency member has specialized services to offer.

The Hospital Staff

Hospital staff first discuss with a patient the possibility of moving into the apartment. The hospital social worker usually has established a relationship with the patient during her hospitalization. This relationship is tremendously supportive to the patient while she is considering moving into the apartment. Continuance of this relationship during the patient's adjustment to the community is helpful.

The hospital psychiatrist is also helpful to the patient in reaching a decision about moving into the apartment. He continues to be available after the patient leaves the hospital. As has been noted, the hospital maintains medical responsibility for the patient.

Massachusetts Rehabilitation Commission

Many patients have become clients of the Rehabilitation Commission while they were in the hospital. After they have moved into the apartment, these individuals continue to receive counseling until their employment situations have become stable. If a resident later becomes unemployed, the counselor is again available. The Commission can provide a maintenance allowance for a short period of time while employment is being obtained.

Brookline Association for Mental Health

Many patients, while in the hospital, form meaningful relationships with volunteers. Continuity of these relationships is particularly important during the period of adjustment to the community. The volunteers are community friends freely available to provide assurance and support to the residents. Volunteers also assist in management of the apartment. They offer personal services, widen community contact, and find employment opportunities.

The executive director of the association is chiefly responsible for handling administrative problems concerning operation of the apartment.

The association also provides financial aid to residents who become unemployed and cannot support themselves. Residents have been allowed to incur a debt for as long as necessary. These residents have always honored their debts, either by direct payment or by doing some office work for the association at a paid hourly rate.

Brookline Mental Health Center

Once a resident arrives at the apartment, the clinic psychiatric social worker assigned to the apartment assumes responsibility for coordination of all related agencies. This social worker meets weekly with the residents in a group and sees them individually as needed.

The group meetings deal with interpersonal relationships, social activities, employment problems, and apartment issues such as maintenance, policy matters, and complaints. Major consideration is given to relationships among apartment members. The emotional disruption caused by people moving in and out of the apartment requires special attention. Emphasis is placed on residents' helping one another. One resident's personal experience can be of significant help to another. For example, the anxiety of a resident who has just come to the apartment can be greatly allayed by others' discussing their feelings when they were faced with the same situation.

PSYCHIATRIC FOLLOW-UP CARE

Aftercare for the residents can be separated into two categories: scheduled treatment and emergency treatment.

For the first sixteen months of the project, residents discharged from Metropolitan State Hospital were followed at the hospital's outpatient clinic. However, since February, 1965, an aftercare evening clinic has been held in the Brookline Mental Health Center, staffed by a hospital psychiatrist and a Brookline Mental Health Center secretary and social worker. This clinic service provides a more convenient location and time for patients; it offers regular contact with the same psychiatrist; it enhances communication between hospital staff and community agencies. Medication from the hospital pharmacy can be dispensed without charge if the resident's budget does not allow for this expenditure. Follow-up care continues to be available after residents have left the apartment. Some residents receive psychiatric treatment at other community facilities or by private psychiatrists.

Emergency ("crisis") treatment for the residents involves twenty-four hour, seven day-a-week availability of one or more of the following: volunteers, the Brookline clinic social worker and psychiatrist, the aftercare clinic psychiatrist. Volunteers can often help a resident through a crisis with their support, encouragement and understanding. If a resident is very disturbed, professional skill of the social worker or the psychiatrist may be needed. Some residents have been seen daily for a short period by various lay and professional people in order to help them through a difficult time. Sometimes the social worker can assist other apartment members to help the disturbed resident. The aftercare clinic psychiatrist is frequently contacted in the evening hours and on weekends. On only one occasion has it been necessary for a staff person to go to the apartment in the late evening hours.

Immediate attention to crisis situations is of vital importance. Hopefully, all possible solutions can be explored, allowing the patient to grow through mastery of the problem rather than meet defeat.

THE RESIDENTS

In the two years since the apartment was established, seventeen patients have resided there. All had a history of hospitalization for mental illness. The majority had been hospitalized for less than two years. Their diagnoses ranged from severe neurotic condition to psychosis; some had alcoholic and suicidal histories. Their ages ranged from nineteen to fifty-one years with an average age of thirty years. Eleven (65 per cent) were single; the rest widowed,

separated or divorced. The average educational level was completion of high school, with a range from eighth grade to a graduate
degree. Most obtained financial help from the Rehabilitation
Commission.

Length of stay in the apartment has ranged from several weeks
to fifteen months, as determined by the individual's emotional,
social and economic needs. Of seventeen women who have lived
in the apartment, four are still living there. The average period of
residence was seven months. Of nine women who lived in the
apartment for more than one month, eight moved into more independent settings from the apartment while the other one returned
to the hospital from the apartment. Of the eight, seven continue to
live in the community.

The minimum period of time that a resident has been away
from the apartment is two months and the maximum fifteen months
with an average of eleven months. All seven ex-residents who continue to live in the community receive follow-up treatment: five
at the Brookline clinic and two at other facilities. The other
woman who moved from the apartment remained in the community for seven months before returning to the hospital; she had
refused follow-up care.

It is evident to us that follow-up care is important since all
seven ex-residents who are still living in the community continue
to receive psychiatric care. These seven women have continued to
make progress: that is, living more independently and responsibly
and forming closer personal relationships. One has established a
home for her two children and another has married.

Of the four residents who moved out of the apartment in less
than one month, the following occurred: two returned directly to
the hospital; one returned to her family but later was rehospitalized;
the fourth moved into a halfway house, having come to the apartment on a temporary basis.

These statistics reveal that 77 per cent of women who resided
in the apartment for longer than a month have been able to adjust
to further independent living in the community. Furthermore, this
data shows that 100 per cent of those residents who left the apartment after a month or more but continued in follow-up care have
been able to maintain themselves in the community.

IMPRESSIONS

Residents have come to the same conclusions about the cooperative apartment experience as the supervisory people. It provides time for transition, provides an address and telephone number without the stigma of a mental hospital, provides a way at minimum cost to try to resume independent and responsible living; provides an opportunity to relearn and to increase social skills; in short, a chance to maintain oneself in a manner which typifies our society.

One of the most significant developments has been willingness of residents to give each other support, assistance and encouragement. Although there have been arguments, disagreements, and tense moments among them, nevertheless, they understand and empathize with each other's emotional needs and rise to demands of the occasion. The social worker has made effective use of this helping relationship for mutual benefit of those who help and those who are helped.

The negative features are lack of privacy, difficulty of living with people who are sometimes incompatible, and disruptive effect of people moving in and out.

CONCLUSION

The cooperative apartment of the Brookline Association for Mental Health has demonstrated that the community can accommodate selected former patients in a temporary semisupervised residence, utilizing a living environment which is characteristic of the community. The anonymity of the apartment allows it to be a typical community residence. These housing facilities are an important part of the rehabilitation process and can help to further community adjustment of former patients.

We have learned that residents of different ages, socioeconomic and educational backgrounds, and varied emotional conditions can live together and adjust satisfactorily. At this time, it is still difficult to predict which patients cannot adjust to the apartment. It appears that patients who have little or no experience in independent living, such as adolescents or those who have been hospitalized since adolescence, are unsuitable apartment residents, or at least great risks.

The availability of financial assistance is extremely important.

Without the security of maintenance funds from the Rehabilitation Commission, some residents would be faced with an anxiety-provoking reality which would add to the stress of their initial community adjustment. For residents who temporarily become unable to support themselves, financial assistance provided by the association allows them to remain in the community and to work toward more independent functioning.

The most important feature in making this program successful is the twenty-four-hour-a-day availability of volunteers and professional persons. This service has helped residents to cope with crises so that their self-confidence was increased; if this service were not available, patients would frequently have met defeat and become discouraged. Availability of this service and regular follow-up care is vital to persons who leave the apartment if they are to maintain the progress made while living there.

It is obvious that this venture is very time-consuming, and no attempt has been made to tabulate the cost of staff time. Excluding this expense and the initial capital outlay, the apartment has proven to be self-supporting.

Present results indicate that selected patients who are provided a semisupervised residence and well-coordinated rehabilitation and aftercare services can become independent and well-functioning community citizens.

Because of the success of this cooperative apartment for women patients, a similar apartment for male patients was opened in January, 1965. It is too soon to make any significant comparisons, although at this point, it would appear that the two have a great deal in common.

Chapter 13

THE ROLE OF VOLUNTEERS IN CENTER CLUB

SAMUEL GROB, Ph.D.*

V OLUNTEERISM has been, in theory and practice, an essential part of *Center Club* philosophy and program since the club's inception in 1959. This will become clear as we attempt to describe the club's organization and to delineate its *modus operandi*.

Center Club is a community center for discharged mental patients.[1] It serves those who need and desire assistance to make the difficult transition from dependent institutional life to the relative independence, self-sufficiency, and self-realization of normal community life. It was created as a result of studies conducted by the Massachusetts Association for Mental Health, Inc., under Vocational Rehabilitation Administration grants dealing with employment prospects and problems of discharged mental patients.[2]

Many vocational difficulties reported seemed to result not so much from lack of vocational skills, training, aptitude, or intelligence as from sheer inability to get along with people. We viewed these difficulties as lingering symptoms of mental illness from which patients were endeavoring to extricate themselves.[3]

It seemed logical, therefore, to develop a community center

*Executive Director
Center House Foundation
Center Club
48 Boylston Street
Boston, Mass.

[1] The author wishes to acknowledge leadership of Mrs. Grenville Clark and Dr. G. Colket Caner, President of the Center House Foundation, in developing broad community concern.

[2] Olshansky, S., Grob, S., and Malamud, I. T.: Employers' attitudes and practices in the hiring of ex-mental patients. *Ment Hyg, 42*:391-401, 1958.

[3] Olshansky, S., Grob, S., Ekdahl, M.: Survey of employment experiences of patients discharged from three state mental hospitals during period 1951-1953. *Ment Hyg, 44*:510-521, 1960.

where discharged patients could participate in a *process of social-ization* leading to more adaptive social behavior. In this specially-created community setting, former patients would be offered acceptance, understanding, practical help, and professional guidance.

The club form evolved from a series of weekly informal meetings initiated by the writer with a small number of recently-discharged mental patients. These patients had come separately to the office of the Massachusetts Association for Mental Health early in 1958 seeking some kind of help. After six months, arrangements were made by a volunteer for subsequent meetings to be held in a church in Boston.

Social meetings were held at the church on one evening each week attended by only six members, a professional and a non-professional volunteer, and the writer. When after a short time it became necessary to have planning meetings on an additional evening of the week, another volunteer made her home available.

In this manner, membership steadily increased to well over one hundred, often with as many as fifty people attending the weekly meeting. Because of its growth the club moved in September, 1960, to its present location, the third floor of the Boston YMC Union Building. This site is centrally located and easily accessible to public transportation. New quarters permitted expansion of the program to fulltime status. A three-year grant was obtained from the Vocation Rehabilitation Administration for a project entitled *Prevocational Planning and Work Conditioning for Selected Ex-mental Patients in a Halfway Social Rehabilitation Center.*[4]

Under the stimulus of increased facilities and staff furnished by the grant, membership and program continued to grow. The only other club in Massachusetts at the time, *103 Club* pioneered by Boston Psychopathic Hospital, now Massachusetts Mental Health Center, was encouraged by its superintendent to merge with *Center Club.*

Club quarters include three rooms for office work; three large rooms for social, recreational, creative arts, or vocational group activities; one small room for research; a kitchen; a large audi-torium and stage for dramatics, dancing and public events. The

[4] Grob, S.: Prevocational planning and work conditioning for seriously handicapped ex-mental patients: a preliminary report. *Ment Hyg, 47*:249-260, 1963.

club is open continuously, Monday through Friday, from 9:30 A.M. to 10:00 P.M.; Saturday, 10:00 A.M. to 5:00 P.M.; Sunday, 2:00 P.M. to 6:00 P.M. Active members now number well over two hundred and fifty.

The club is used as an *activity* center with major emphasis on dynamics of group process as leverage for individual progress. Planning, conduct, and evaluation of all programs are to be accomplished by club members, in cooperation with staff and volunteers.

Activities are mainly concrete and realistic. They are oriented away from self-preoccupation, toward objects and interests possessing intrinsic appeal and value. Put another way, we focus upon whatever ego strength we can find and build on it no matter how small the basis may be. We utilize the technique of environmental manipulation, rather than intrapsychic exploration, to advance the adaptive strength of members.

The club concept implies that program content must utilize members' interests and initiative. Members are encouraged to participate with volunteers and staff in the process of self-government, program planning, community education, research, and fund-raising. The roles to be developed are complementary and functional rather than hierarchical.[5]

Guidance of behavior is effected by offering suitable role models in the persons of staff and volunteers. Informal counseling is carried on by staff personnel in all individual and group situations. Formal and informal conferences are frequently held between volunteers and staff in order to review experiences and to develop more effective performance.

This model, particularly in its motivational aspects, is derived principally from social system and role theory, enriched with personality theory. It is conceived as an adjunct to the traditional medical model which emphasizes the patient-doctor relationship.

Focusing upon behavioral rather than verbal patterns of interaction, the staff encourages members to identify with qualities of initiative, self-reliance, and mutual aid. Natural motivation for

---

[5] Grob, S., ed.: *The Community Social Club and the Returning Mental Patient*. Proceedings of an NIMH Conference, Framingham, Mass., November, 1963. (Available from Center Club, 48 Boylston St., Boston, Mass.)

self-restoration is emphasized so that a member's potential resources may be released. This model has been found appropriate in its empirical as well as its theoretical aspects to cope with problems of this population.

Volunteers constitute a vital part of the system. They can enter any aspect of club activity, whether social, recreational, artistic, vocational, educational, or fund-raising. Participation is limited only by their security, maturity, and objectivity.

Over the years, we have had a great variety of volunteers from all walks of life, all ages, religions, races and classes. We could never pay for the services rendered by these people any more than they could fully evaluate the impact of this experience and training for their personal lives.

Both student and adult volunteers have come to us through organized as well as individual channels. Students have come from neighboring universities as part of a course assignment or through their own initiative. We prefer that they participate as part of their course work. They have shown considerable aptitude for contributing to our activities. Their youthfulness is no bar to healthy interaction with older members, other volunteers, or staff. They respond well to supervision and develop rapidly with experience.

Countless adult volunteers with skills in art, music, dancing, dramatics, crafts, sewing, culinary arts, or sports have provided leadership in group activities. In turn, they are given support and guidance by professional staff.

The breadth of our program makes it attractive to increasing numbers of volunteers who become interested in the mental health field. Additional inducements are our community setting, cooperative approach, and challenging opportunities to meet needs of seriously handicapped discharged patients.

Our major problem at the present time is a consequence of our continued growth and vitality: the limitation of professional staff time for guidance and supervision of volunteer work. As we have learned, this is a serious problem. The value of volunteers is directly proportional to the availability of sound professional coverage, and inversely proportional to the sheer amount of unsupervised involvement. The loss deriving from lack of guidance does not refer to endangering the welfare of members; the loss is sustained in failing to utilize fully the resources of dedicated volunteers.

We do not subscribe to the notion that volunteers may be less valuable to us than professional persons. The essential difference, in our view, lies in the know-how, stability, and continuity imparted to the system and program by paid professional staff. Without this underpinning there could be no club as we know it, or volunteers participating in it. By the same token, this program could not achieve its present objectives without volunteers' playing a part in the vary warp and woof of the organization. It is precisely in this respect that we depart from the traditional clinic, social agency, hospital, or other highly formalized institution.

At the present time, we can classify our volunteers into three categories according to the nature of their involvement in *Center Club*. The first group of about twenty-five equally comprised of adults and students participate with members in various activities on a weekly schedule throughout the year. The second group, consisting of about seventy-five people, constitutes an auxiliary whose major contribution is public relations, community education, and minor fund-raising for specific projects. The third group, consisting of twenty-seven prominent community leaders, constitutes the *Center House Foundation,* which assumes the major responsibility for generating voluntary financial support.

In addition to these major groups, many other individuals intermittently contribute their time, energy, interest, and money usually in connection with some event, performance, or project in which they may be particularly interested.

The paid staff currently consists of three fulltime, two half-time and six part-time people who provide coverage for a seventy-four hour week. These figures clearly indicate that, although the extent of volunteer help may be not as visible as we would like, it is far from inconsiderable even in this early stage of development.

I believe that we have demonstrated our program to be a valuable adjunctive service to psychiatric facilities, without which uncounted individuals would be unable to achieve a satisfactory return to community life. Furthermore, because members and volunteers assume a portion of the operational costs, these results can be obtained on a relatively small budget. These contributions are an integral part of a joint effort to promote recovery and rehabilitation.

The benefits of this program, both human and financial, can be multiplied indefinitely by incorporating a therapeutic social club in any community mental health service. Our special orientation utilizes a large manpower pool from the adjunctive fields enabling us to free medical personnel for other therapeutic work.

We have shown that our volunteers can assist greatly in restoring normal social behavior. With modest increments of staff and money, much more could be done in the areas of physical fitness, nutrition, family counseling, housing, and employment to strengthen members' resources for independent living and personal adjustment.

Chapter 14

THE TORCHLIGHTERS CLUB

EILEEN CORNING*

AFTER PATIENTS have been discharged from a large mental hospital, there may be little follow-up to determine their success in readjusting to community life. Many isolate themselves as much as possible and exist almost in a world of their own. This situation is worse than hospital life since in the hospital patients may have some sociability. When it is suggested that patients return to their former neighborhoods some feel that they will be uncomfortable, that their old friends have turned against them. If, on the other hand, a patient contemplates living in a completely new neighborhood, he may be afraid because he does not know anyone. Some former patients will not even attempt an activity such as church attendance because they are afraid of not being accepted.

With growing concern for the problems faced by discharged patients, discussions were carried on by the Rehabilitation Committee of the Mental Health Association of the North Shore.[1] Several members of this committee had been working with patients at nearby Danvers State Hospital.

A committee of ten volunteers decided to attempt the organization of a strictly social club. Its goal was to assist discharged patients to make a satisfying adjustment to the community.

Before the club opened in October, 1963, the volunteers had numerous consultations with a psychologist. It was decided that the psychologist would organize meetings and long range plans,

*Rehabilitation Committee
 Mental Health Association of the North Shore
 One Cambridge Street
 Salem, Mass.

[1] The author wishes to acknowledge the assistance of Tobias Friedman, M.D., and Mrs. Harry I. Hilliard.

while volunteers would provide transportation and companionship at the meetings. The association would assume the cost of the psychologist's services. Arrangements were established for meetings one evening each week, between 7:30 P.M. and 9:30 P.M., from October through May.

The only requirement for club membership was experience in psychiatric treatment. As for volunteers, they had to be willing to attend meetings one evening a week. Most important, they had to possess a sincere interest in working with former patients and in helping them to make a more personally satisfying adjustment to the community. After the first year of professional guidance, the club was able to carry on, staffed solely by volunteers in a relaxed and social way.

A major problem which only time could solve was, "How would this club become known?" Should volunteers broach the idea to persons who had been under psychiatric care, or would these people resent such a suggestion? Actually, much to the pleasure of the volunteers, the club increased its membership by word of mouth. At first, membership was very small but given time, the members themselves were the best source of referrals. They were already familiar with several persons who had been in the hospital or under psychiatric care at the same time as they had been. As one member expressed her interest, "I joined the *Torchlighters Club* because I needed an interest other than my work. I also needed to get out, meet people and see things . . ."

Initial membership was only four persons and within less than one year's time, the membership had grown to well over twenty. As enthusiasm increased, the members decided that some formal structure was desirable. They set down a few procedures for electing a chairman and other officers. At about the same time, they established their present name of the *Torchlighters Club*.

Activities which evoked greatest interest among members were travelogue color movies with sound track, bowling parties and square dancing instruction.

All of these were furnished once a month without charge by interested local citizens. In an article in the *Torchlighter Newsletter,* the following was written:

> We salute Paul Channel and Bob Barker for many enjoyable

evenings of square dancing. These volunteers add much to the success of our club. Several couples from their group have joined to help with various dances. *Many Thanks.*

Excursions and birthday or holiday buffet suppers are a real treat. The *Newsletter* carried the following item:

> A delightful evening was enjoyed at the Ice Follies in the Boston Garden. Eighteen members and eight volunteers went by bus and had a gay songfest, to and from Boston.

> August 17—We had a lovely boat ride around Marblehead Harbor. Immediately following we had Pot Luck supper at the home of a volunteer. *Yummy.*

These events are planned and provided by the members with a minimum of help from volunteers. Occasionallly, the club enjoys a quiet social evening with coffee and cookies provided by members.

Assisting in community projects is a regular club activity. For example, an evening was spent in the Essex County Health Association office, preparing envelopes for its Christmas appeal. The members worked very constructively for the benefit of the community.

The club's present meeting room is furnished by a local bank which has a large basement room with kitchen facilities. It is well lighted and heated and has ample room for various activities. The bank is situated in the center of the North Shore area, making transportation as convenient as possible. One of the year's highlights was a recent meeting at which Torchlighters had an opportunity to entertain members of a similar club (See Chapter 13.) Another news item:

> On August 6, the *Center Club* of Boston came to Lynch Park, Beverly, as our guests. Twenty-five members came by bus and seemed to have a great time. The event was perfect with mountains of food and coffee . . . Planning this was just as much fun as the event itself.

One outstanding evening this past summer, was a "cookout" held at the home of one of the members. This affair was planned and served entirely by the members, as a salute to the volunteers, complete with poetry dedicated to the guests. News item:

> July 20th—the members entertained the volunteers at a cook-

out at Helen Adams' home. We all had a wonderful time with
lots of laughs when Marion Gordon arrived in a very funny out-
fit. She wrote a clever poem dedicated to the volunteers.
  Many thanks for a grand evening.

Our latest project has been the establishing of a newsletter. The
Torchlighter is now sent to members, volunteers, and community
leaders six times a year. A committee of four or five members helps
to write about past activities and list future meetings and plans.
This newsletter provides a calendar of events for the following
two months and helps to keep members informed of all club
activities. A volunteer is on hand to advise the members.

Many members are able to furnish their own transportation to
and from the meetings while others are dependent on a volunteer.
Several members are in rest homes or in isolated areas where public
transportation cannot be provided. This club has included members
from approximately six cities and towns on the North Shore covering a radius of about twelve miles. The transportation problem is
shared by several volunteers.

Volunteers find they are often called upon to visit members in
their homes. Many problems are discussed and a solution is worked
out, contacting the proper authority when necessary. For example,
locating jobs and solving problems of transportation to work, and
helping to locate rooms and apartments for members require extra
effort on the part of the volunteers. Another very important task
is encouragement of members to keep a continual check on their
health, with return visits to the hospital as recommended by their
doctors.

The philosophy behind the *Torchlighters Club,* simply stated,
is to aid in establishing better individual and group relationships
and to give members a renewed sense of belonging and participating in the community. This strictly social club, with both men and
women members, is one of the many stepping stones in helping
a former patient to gain a better understanding of himself and
society.

Looking into the future, it is the hope of volunteers and members
to increase the *Torchlighters Club* membership to a much larger
number, to organize activities on a daily, rather than a weekly,
basis and to succeed eventually in maintaining a social center
which is professionally staffed and heavily supported by volunteers.

Chapter 15

THE CONCEPT OF A SOCIAL AIDE ORGANIZATION

MARY DAVIS*

W ORK OF VOLUNTEERS for the mentally ill has traditionally taken place in the hospital. In recent years, however, with change of attitudes and change of treatment, a need has been expressed for volunteers to work with patients as they prepare to leave the hospital and during their adjustment to the community.

There seem to be emerging two categories of volunteers for the mentally ill. The first might be called an *in-service aide,* one who gives service to patients during hospitalization. The second category might be called a *social aide,* one who helps a patient prepare to leave the hospital and continues to help him during his adjustment to the community.

Many patterns have been demonstrated for work of the in-service aide and the social aide. The question arises as to how these functions can be coordinated to provide continuity of care for the patient. When one speaks of coordination, the words administration, organization, training and program come to mind. It is through these mechanisms that coordination takes place.

In the hospital or clinic, policies and functions for volunteers have been defined and developed. It is in the area of resocialization, during the patient's transition from hospital to community, that volunteer services become uncoordinated. Who has responsibility for administration of the volunteer in the community? Who determines policy in organization, training, professional super-

*Chairman, Volunteer Committee
Massachusetts Association for Mental Health, Inc.
Norfolk Mental Health Association, Inc.
698 Washington Street
Norwood, Mass.

vision, and program? Is this the province of the hospital alone? If not, how, when and where does the community begin to assume these responsibilities?

If the larger community accepts some responsibility for discharged patients, the hospital may continue to serve as a resource. This goal has by no means been achieved as yet. However, unless we devise the ways and means of achieving it, we are probably deluding ourselves in thinking that patients can come back to the community to stay.

I would like to present for your consideration the concept of a social aide organization in the community. As with all community response to a need, the social aide organization begins with a group of citizens motivated to help. This group in turn interests others, and with cooperation of the hospital and of community agencies, develops a social aide organization. A volunteer committee of a mental health association may be an ideal group to initiate such an organization. A social aide program has, in fact, been organized by the author's local mental health association to provide continuity of volunteer services for patients at the Medfield State Hospital. (See Chapter 16.) However, any interested group of citizens could provide impetus for a social aide organization.

The function of a social aide organization is to work with community agencies, organizations and citizens to help the discharged patient find a satisfying niche in society. The social aides, as a group, survey their community to determine job opportunities, kinds and cost of available living quarters, religious institutions, social resources such as YMCA, hobby and neighborhood clubs and official community resources such as welfare, public health, educational and recreational activities. They work closely with and support programs of the Rehabilitation Commission. They may help former patients to organize a social club if it is needed or desired. A case aide can function within the social aide organization by explaining the specific needs of a patient about to return to the community. (See Chapters 6 and 7.)

Membership for the social aide organization comes from the citizenry but its administrative board has a representative from hospital, community mental health clinic, and community agencies. Policies on recruitment, organization, training and program depend on needs of patients and the leadership and other resources available in the community.

Priority is given to finding a professional person who can provide leadership in determining the program and training, who can provide coordination between hospital, community agencies and volunteers, and who will give continuing supervision to volunteers.

Once there is community interest in helping discharged patients, the social aide organization can be a focus around which activities proliferate. This concept provides for a soundly structured organization under professional supervision which insures comprehensive planning and establishes priorities.

I would like to present a hypothetical case history as an illustration of how a social aide organization could function. The patient in this case history has been placed in a hospital that has a case aide program. Therefore, the work of the case aide in the hospital will be integrated with the work of the social aide in the community. Where there is no case aide program, the social aide organization can relate directly to the hospital programs preparing the patient to return.

Mr. Green has been hospitalized for seven years. He has received the benefit of hospital treatment and volunteer program. The professional staff has now determined that he will soon be ready to leave the hospital. Since he will be returning to the community of Norwood, he has been assigned a case aide who is also from Norwood.

The case aide's professional supervisor contacts the professional supervisor of the social aide organization and together they coordinate the work of the case aide and the social aide organization Responsibilities assumed in this case are under the supervision, direction and guidance of the professional supervisors.

The hospital case aide has learned from Mr. Green the kinds of jobs, living quarters, and social life in which he would be comfortable. Mr. Green has in turn established a sound relationship with this person from his community.

At this stage, while Mr. Green is still in the hospital, the case aide contacts the social aide organization and informs them of Mr. Green's needs. He has a high school education and is capable of working in jobs demanding manual to semiskilled labor.

The social aide then refers to up-to-date files on living quarters to determine what is available for a single man capable of preparing simple meals. She informs the case aide of these living quarters, and the cost and proximity to transportation.

When the problem of living quarters has been resolved, the hospital determines that Mr. Green may leave. During his adjustment to the community, a social aide calls upon him, informs him of her organization, gives him pertinent information about the community, and offers her assistance.

Mr. Green is a Congregationalist and is interested in baseball, fishing and cabinet work. The social aide contacts the minister of the Congregational church in Norwood and through him finds a parishioner to accompany Mr. Green to a Sunday service and to introduce him to the church's social functions. She contacts the *Fish and Game Club* to see if a member will take him fishing and include him in the club activities. She informs Mr. Green of the adult education courses in cabinet making and assists him in applying for admittance to a course.

If difficulty arises in keeping appointments in an aftercare clinic, the social aide can be of assistance.

Through this process, the hospital case aide continues to befriend Mr. Green. Mr. Green then makes a new friendship with a social aide and finally establishes new independent relationships on the job and in social circles.

If a need for rehospitalization occurs, the hospital case aide and social aide again work as a team on arrangements. The social aide in the role of a friend sees that Mr. Green is not forgotten in the community. She enlists the church, the people with whom he has worked, and friends he has made, to visit and write and remember holidays so that when he returns to the community again it will not be as a stranger.

The role of a social aide organization in relation to the community mental health center will become more definitive as community mental health center programs evolve. It will depend on the extent of the center's program and of its professional staff. Since the center will be community based, one can visualize the social aide organization as one of the many community resources the center will draw upon.

In-service aides are people having empathy, understanding and the skill to stimulate and motivate as well as to comfort.

Case aides are people who have the capacity to be comfortable in an interpersonal relationship. They are willing to take time and patience to develop it.

Social aides are people who know the community and can bring about not only action but also understanding.

Many people have all these skills and talent. Can we organize, integrate and coordinate them to provide continuity of care and continuity of caring for those who are and have been mentally ill?

Chapter 16

CONTINUITY OF CARE IN VOLUNTEER SERVICES

IRVING SANDERS, M.A.*

V OLUNTEER SERVICE for the mentally ill is not a new phenomenon. Few state hospitals exist without some type of volunteers who provide at least a modicum of services. Most of these services have had a Topsy-like growth, with little or no planning, usually started on the initiative of some individual or organization extrinsic to the hospital.

Volunteer services in the state hospitals of Massachusetts are as varied as the number of hospitals. Some hospitals make imaginative use of the volunteer while others tread only the most timeworn paths. In the latter group, volunteers are often merely tolerated for their public relations value. These volunteers perform only the most routine work and attain minimal satisfaction from their contacts with the hospital. In some cases, both patients and volunteers derive so little from each other that if the program were terminated neither might feel any sense of loss.

Medfield State Hospital in Harding, Massachusetts, has for some time been aware of the important contribution volunteers can offer to the total treatment program. Orientation of the staff to making the hospital a training and teaching center for all the mental health disciplines provides a milieu which is hospitable to new ways of looking at volunteer services also.

During the past four years, the Norfolk Mental Health Association has been engaged in a number of successful joint ventures with

*Executive Director
Norfolk Mental Health Association, Inc.
698 Washington Street
Norwood, Mass.

the Medfield State Hospital, developing enviable working relationships between the two organizations. Together they have co-sponsored seminars for clergy and mental health careers programs at the high school and college levels. (See Chapter 20.) The association operates a sheltered workshop at the hospital. An additional shared project is the assignment of psychiatric residents for training at the association's child guidance clinic.

With this background of harmonious relationships, the association proposed that the two organizations undertake a demonstration project in joint planning for volunteer services in the hospital and community.

The demonstration project developed in four distinct phases, namely: exploration; "tooling-up"; recruitment, and the plan in action.

PHASE I: EXPLORATION

At the outset, the association formed a steering committee representing five communities served by the association and the hospital. This committee was comprised of persons who had already indicated a strong commitment toward volunteer services. In the fall of 1964, the committee with guidance of the association's executive director and a chairman from the association's board began a series of monthly meetings with the hospital superintendent, volunteer director and key department heads.

The main focus of these meetings was to explore areas of unmet needs for volunteers as viewed by the hospital's key personnel. Needs were pointed out in many areas both within and outside the hospital.

Because of the large variety of volunteer services desired, it was felt that it would be necessary to classify them in terms of their importance as well as feasibility of development. This led naturally to an establishment of priorities.

PHASE II: "TOOLING-UP"

After priorities were agreed upon, the steering committee began to view the program in terms of administrative organization, training, and delivery of services. Continuity of care was viewed as a primary goal. The term "continuity of care" implied a program of volunteer services which begins within the hospital and continues after the patient's return to the community. Community volunteers could offer many services to insure that gains made in therapy within the hospital would be maintained and even extended in the community.

A further step in "tooling-up" the organization was formation of an area executive committee made up of persons designated to be town chairmen. It seemed clear that some services would best be provided on a town-by-town basis, such as a regional class to reacquaint discharged patients with the use of cooking appliances.

PHASE III: RECRUITMENT

Manpower for this program was to be comprised of three categories of volunteers. The first was to be volunteers providing a variety of services to patients and staff within the hospital. A second group was to be persons working on a one-to-one basis with patients under close supervision of staff, namely case aides.

To fill an important gap, the committee proposed a new category of volunteer called the "social aide."

The social aide represents a distinct category of volunteer services directed toward helping discharged patients. Why not call this volunteer a "community volunteer"? Two reasons seem pertinent: (1) The mental hospital should really be viewed as a part of the community. Because most hospitals have traditionally been located "in the sticks," far from the patient's home and serving a large number of communities, the state hospital has been considered "outside" the community. Using the term "community volunteer" reinforces this separation. (2) The social aide concept could be a source of attraction for an entirely different group of citizens who would not wish to serve within the hospital.

A wide variety of responsibility could be assigned to the social aide. They could do the following:

1. Assist in solving the problem of living quarters for discharged patients by surveying private and public resources; work with welfare agencies in placement.

2. Assist in obtaining employment by surveying the community for jobs; provide courses in training for application for employment.

3. Assist in socialization by contacting community, social, religious, and fraternal organizations.

4. Contact lawyers to provide legal information.

5. Contact community resources to provide special programs in "fashion therapy" and arrange with beauticians, clothing and cosmetic suppliers for supplies.

6. Provide assistance to the families of hospitalized patients.

PHASE IV: THE PLAN IN ACTION

Putting the plan in action involved coordination between the association and the hospital. A training program for volunteers was jointly planned. All volunteers receive orientation appropriate to the tasks they are to perform. Work schedules for the volunteers are jointly determined in conference between the association's executive committee and the hospital. Volunteer assignment is also a matter of joint determination.

Flexibility in assignment of volunteers will assure the placing of "round pegs in round holes." Volunteers who can function best in the case aide position can be placed there, while those who cannot tolerate working in a hospital setting can be utilized in the community. Those who fit best in the traditional "in-hospital" positions can be assigned there.

With a variety of assignments, available within the hospital and in the community, it becomes possible to place volunteers where they can serve most effectively. Often volunteers find a need for a new setting. Under this plan, volunteers can be reassigned in order to make best use of their capacities.

At the present writing, sufficient time has not elapsed to determine how the project will ultimately work out. However, the degree of mutual understanding and cooperation which is already evident, and without which such a program could not even be undertaken, augurs well for its success.

Part IV

STUDENTS IN MENTAL HEALTH WORK

Chapter 17

PROFESSIONAL SUPERVISION AS A MEANS OF ACHIEVING VOLUNTEER PROGRAM GOALS

HELEN REINHERZ, Sc.D.*

SUPERVISION is often considered an essential part of volunteer programs. Indeed, numerous articles have been written to describe methods of supervision used in specific projects. However, there have been few systematic examinations of the effects of supervision on volunteers or on overall program goals.

In this chapter, we will discuss a number of issues important to administrators and to professional supervisors of volunteer programs. Among the areas to be investigated are the following:

1. Is there any evidence that professional supervision aids a volunteer in achievement of his own objectives for volunteering?

2. Does professional leadership facilitate achievement of program goals such as creating favorable attitudes toward the mentally ill and/or encouraging entrance into mental health careers?

3. What are the important tasks of a professional person working with student volunteers?

4. What are the professional and personal qualities of supervisors designated as having the most positive effect?

To answer these questions the author will draw on personal experience as a supervisor of volunteers as well as on results of a longitudinal study[1] of one hundred and twenty-nine Harvard-Rad-

*Associate Professor
Simmons College School of Social Work
51 Commonwealth Avenue
Boston, Mass.

[1] The author wishes to acknowledge that the base-line data for follow-up was secured from a study financed by P.H.S. Grant #O.M. 233, directed by David Kantor. Ph.D.

111

cliffe students who were first-time volunteers in the Phillips Brooks House Program at the Metropolitan State Hospital in 1959 and 1960.[2]

SOME UNIVERSAL GOALS OF VOLUNTEERS IN THE HEALTH FIELD: THEIR RELATIONSHIP TO VOLUNTEER SATISFACTION AND MORALE

No volunteer program, no matter how thoughtful in conception or essential in fulfilling a need, can be maintained without continued participation of a nucleus of volunteers. Volunteer "drop out" can impair program efficiency as well as morale. In fact, one volunteer administrator has observed that "dropping out" can be considered a most serious infectious disease since it affects morale of other professional and volunteer participants and has been known to spread rapidly. There is substantial evidence that an individual's continued participation is directly related to his major reasons for volunteering.

Major Stated Motivations for Volunteering

The majority of one hundred and twenty-nine first-time volunteers in the Phillips Brooks House program, as well as those in the only published large-scale study of all ages,[3] stated that they volunteered for two major reasons: *to learn* and *to help those in need.*

There is no doubt that the objectives of *helping patients* and *learning about mental illness* are expedited and often obtainable only through carefully planned supervisory experiences. Direct evidence of this is found in behavior and statements of Harvard-Radcliffe volunteers. Volunteers who spent less than a semester in the Harvard-Radcliffe program in 1959 and 1960 were, in most instances, not in groups that had access to regular professional supervision. Seventy-five per cent of the "dropouts" (those who left before finishing a semester of participation) were not in groups

---

[2] The material presented in this chapter is selected from the author's doctoral dissertation, Harvard School of Public Health: *A Follow-up Study of Student Volunteers in a Mental Hospital.* April, 1965. This study is currently being revised for publication under the title *A Crack in the Door.*

[3] Sills, D.L.: *The Volunteer—Means and Ends in a National Organization.* Glencoe, Free Press, 1957.

with professional supervisors. In contrast, the majority of those remaining for a year or longer had regular professional supervision.

One student who dropped out after a few visits to the hospital said:

> There was no one to guide our group, to tell us whether what we did was helping or hurting patients. I never learned anything about a single patient.

In contrast, a student who was spending his fourth year in the Phillips Brooks House program said:

> In a sense, the professional supervisor's work with our group can be described as sensitizing us to the needs of the patients and our own activities in handling these needs . . . As students we naturally place a high value upon learning. Thus, we find ourselves receiving an education in the problems of mental health and in psychology through discussing our actual experiences and of course, ourselves . . .

From the statements above, as well as indications of satisfaction or dissatisfaction expressed by length of stay in the program, the volunteers indicated that supervision had value for them both in enabling them to help patients and in learning about the complex problems of mental health.

SUPERVISION AS IT AFFECTS MAJOR GOALS OF A STUDENT VOLUNTEER PROGRAM

The focus of discussion now turns to goals of programs organized for students or other young people. A reader may readily see that most of these goals are applicable to volunteers of all ages.

Major priorities of volunteer programs in the mental health field include service to patients as well as a universal aim to increase understanding of mental health problems. It is hoped that volunteers may in turn convey more positive attitudes to the communities from which they come.

When youthful volunteers are the main participants in a program, an additional goal may be to provide an incentive for selecting a mental health career. This last aim is made more urgent in an era when needs are growing at an enormous rate while the manpower pool is increasing to a smaller degree.

In the next section of this chapter, evidence will be presented that achievement of all these goals was closely related to presence or absence of professional leadership.

Service to Patients

An important aspect of service is continuity of the relationship since many patients have frequently been subjected to broken relationships with other human beings. Continuation of service for a year or longer also allows a volunteer to become comfortable in the hospital setting. He can form meaningful relationships with individual patients or groups. He can provide leadership and serve as a role model and recruiting agent for underclassmen.

The follow-up study clearly showed a positive relationship between *continuation in the program for longer periods* (over one year) and *professional supervision*. Thus, the important requirement for stability of service is the presence of a trained leader.

The Link between Professional Leadership and Attitudinal Change

The report of the *Joint Commission on Mental Illness and Health*[4] firmly underlined the need for altering attitudes of indifference toward the mentally ill held by potentially influential citizens. This was seen as a major step in creating a climate favorable to improved treatment. Since students are at a particularly impressionable and fluid stage of their development, the experience of volunteering in a mental hospital can have tremendous attitudinal impact.

As one gifted girl, who became a journalist after college, said of her year as a case-aide at Metropolitan State Hospital:

> It opened a crack in the door to a totally new world . . . it removed my previous feeling that insanity was something shameful, shocking. It increased my comprehension of the human mind . . . and helped me to have humility before it.

A boy in medical school said:

> Before going to the hospital I thought of psychotics as caged animals. While doing volunteer work, I learned that these patients

[4] Joint Commission on Mental Illness and Health: *Action for Mental Health. Final Report.* New York, Basic Books, 1961.

were people and I formed bonds of friendship with some of them . . . The living conditions were terrible. We need to spend much more for mental health care. I realize that it is easy now I'm away to forget about the hospital and the patients. I try not to.

The two responses just quoted were selected from those indicating a *positive* attitudinal impact of the volunteer experience. Other students, although in the minority, indicated that the experience had a *negative* impact. For example, one student said, "It showed me I wasn't cut out for mental health work." Another said:

It convinced me that I do not enjoy it sufficiently to ever do it again . . . As a meaningful experience it served little purpose.

Analysis of responses of the one hundred and twenty-nine students indicated that 72 per cent of those who had regular professional supervision assessed the impact of the experience as *positive*. On the other hand, only 41 per cent of those *without* professional supervision indicated a favorable impact on their attitudes and lives.

Although the overall effect of the program can be discussed only in part in the present article, the author's more lengthy treatment of the study considers attitudinal change as the most salient attribute of the Harvard program. The marked association between increase in *positive* mental health attitudes and participation in a professionally guided group must be noted here, however briefly.

Mental Health Career Choice and Contact with Mental Health Professional Staff

One of the most important goals (sometimes overt and sometimes implicit) of student volunteer programs is providing an incentive for entrance into mental health work. To determine what factors in the experience were significant, actual occupational choices of Harvard-Radcliffe volunteers were examined in the follow-up period several years after their entering the program. Discussion of specific mental-health-related choices can be covered only in summary. The fact that a large proportion of students chose careers in fields related to mental health work, such as general medicine and teaching, must also await full discussion in a complete report.

However, a significantly larger proportion of those preparing for careers in mental health (psychiatry, psychology, social work) had participated in groups with regular professional supervision. Those choosing mental health careers also indicated much more frequent contact with greater numbers and kinds of hospital personnel than did most volunteers not choosing careers in mental health.

In addition to this quantitative indication, students in interviews and written statements gave personal examples of reactions to professional persons encountered in their volunteer work. For example, one girl who was completing her second year at a school of social work said of her supervisor:

> Mrs. X showed me what a social worker could be both by her example and by her help to me at a time when I was confused about personal and career plans . . .

One salient characteristic mentioned by students as an influence on career plans was a supervisor's *own interest* and dedication to his work.

A boy in medical school planning to specialize in psychiatry said:

> I valued the opportunity to learn about an important problem (mental illness). But most important was the chance to see dedicated human beings sympathetically involved in wholeheartedly trying to solve the problem.

In a variety of ways, students indicated that when a decision had been made to change a career choice, contact with professional workers had been important. However, they did not always specify what facet of the supervisor's behavior or personality was most important.

One student who changed his career choice from literature to psychiatry simply listed six staff members with whom he had had contact in the program. He said, "This is why I decided to work in the mental health field." There is considerable evidence for concluding that in the minds of students who made career changes the professional persons with whom they had contact were influential.

THE TASKS OF THE SUPERVISOR IN VOLUNTEER PROGRAMS WITH STUDENTS

The preceding section of this chapter indicated that students who decided to pursue mental health careers acknowledged the influence of professional persons in the program. In a paper I wrote some time ago, I mentioned a number of other important tasks of the supervisor in a mental hospital program involving young volunteers.[5] In addition to providing a professional role model, the supervisor has the tasks of teaching about mental health as well as about the specific needs of patients. A staff member also has the function of providing emotional support for late-adolescent volunteers working with very ill patients.

In this chapter I shall stress a facet of the supervisor's job that has not received as much attention as the *career-inducing* and *teaching* functions. Very important in the follow-up study was the supervisor's role in *providing emotional support and being available for on-the-spot consultation.* There was a sizeable group of volunteers (22 per cent of the total) who mentioned that they experienced a threat to their own emotional equilibrium during their participation in the program. The amount of upset and the degree to which it affected their functioning varied from slight to considerable. However, feelings most often mentioned were a sense of inadequacy and one of depression.

Under the "self-screening" system of the Phillips Brooks House Mental Hospital Program, volunteers who felt too upset or too threatened left the program. Volunteers who said they were "upset by the experience" also rated the impact of the program in negative terms; they made up a large part of the "dropout" group.

Such evidence reinforces the importance of access to professional consultation and support. Volunteers who found the program too demanding or upsetting might still have been free to leave after professional consultation. However, it seems likely that with more understanding of the experience, they might have turned to a new activity or program more freely.

VOLUNTEERS' ASSESSMENT OF LEADERS

Volunteers' assessment of professional leaders reveals qualities felt to be beneficial in the supervisory experience. Information of this nature may prove useful to those who select leaders for similar programs. When results were analyzed, a rather clear-cut pattern

---

[5] Reinherz, H.; Leadership of student volunteers. *Ment Hosp,* 13:600-602, 1962.

emerged describing qualities found beneficial and others found undesirable.

From the volunteer's view, a good leader had sound understanding of patients, hospital, volunteers, and group interaction. A poor leader failed to have mastery of some or all of these areas. The ideal leader presented a sense of being committed to patients, students, and his profession. The poor leader seemed to have a passive attitude and appeared not to "care."

According to the volunteers' reports, the good leader has ability to convey his understanding and feelings to the group. Verbally and by behavior, he demonstrated interest in the problems of students, whether related to work with patients, to interaction among volunteers, or to the impact of the volunteer experience. The poor leader, in spite of technical understanding or knowledge, was seen as unable or even unwilling to share this knowledge with students.

In speaking of a leader rated most positively by all students, a volunteer said:

> My leader was, first of all, an open and warm person who created freedom of expression in our group. He had a genuine interest in the volunteer and his own work. Most of all he was *most worthy of respect.*

Adjectives used to describe positive characteristics of leaders were *perceptive, inspirational, involved, committed, congenial, motivating.* On the other hand, negative adjectives were *uninteresting, boring, domineering, insincere,* and *unsympathetic.*

In summary, the students seemed to respond best to a competent professional person who was able to convey a sense of interest and commitment toward his professional role and toward his leadership tasks with the volunteer group.

SUMMARY OF SALIENT DIMENSIONS OF SUPERVISION OF STUDENT VOLUNTEERS

Using results of one of the few objective studies of the impact of volunteering, some ideas and evidence have been presented to demonstrate the extent to which volunteers' major goals are expedited by provision of professional supervision.

In addition, material has been provided to illustrate that major goals of administrators of student volunteer programs, including attitudinal and career change, were also facilitated by professional guidance.

Finally, volunteers' opinions of qualities for successful professional leadership were discussed as possible guides to those who have the task of providing leadership for similar programs.

Chapter 18

HIDDEN ASSETS:
A YOUTH VOLUNTEER PROGRAM IN A
PSYCHIATRIC HOSPITAL

REBECCA GLASMANN, A.C.S.W.*

RUTH TURNER†

IN THIS CHAPTER, we will discuss the unique program of the Arlington High School Youth Volunteers at the Bedford Veterans Administration Hospital, and we will demonstrate the great potential of such a project.[1]

DEVELOPMENT OF COOPERATIVE PROJECT IN THE COMMUNITY

Why was the Arlington High School-Bedford Veterans Administration Hospital Youth Volunteer Program started? Because inherent in many young people is a desire to be helpful to others, and at Bedford, there was a growing need for volunteers to work with our population of patients who are over sixty years of age.

The chief social worker at Bedford as a member of the Board of Directors of the Arlington Mental Health Association presented,

*Chief, Social Work Service
Veterans Administration Hospital
200 Springs Road
Bedford, Mass.

†Assistant Director, Volunteer Services
Veterans Administration Hospital
200 Springs Road
Bedford, Mass.

[1] The authors wish to acknowledge assistance of the following persons in this project: Dr. Bert Roens, Superintendent of Schools, Arlington, Mass.; Mrs. Chester F. Protheroe, President, Arlington Mental Health Association, Arlington, Mass.: Mr. Charles H. Downs, Principal, Arlington High School, Arlington, Mass.; S.P. LaCerva, M.D., Hospital Director, Veterans Administration Hospital, Bedford, Mass.

in May, 1961, a blueprint for a youth volunteer program with the cooperation of the Arlington High School and the Bedford Veterans Administration Hospital. The superintendent of schools, also a board member, gave full support to the development of such a program and it was given board approval. Then began a series of meetings with the superintendent of schools so that he would become familiar with the hospital's goals and its philosophy relating to volunteers, specifically to youth volunteers. It was expected that no more than ten students would be involved during the school year 1961-1962. The Arlington Mental Health Association, besides underwriting the cost of uniforms, would also make available adult volunteers to chauffeur the children from the high school to the hospital and return.

The superintendent of schools talked with the school principal and the guidance teachers about the opportunities of this program. The high school had for several years sent selected students to nearby settlement houses and general hospitals, but had never made use of psychiatric hospitals.

The superintendent invited the chief social worker to discuss the program with the principal and guidance teachers. There were questions and discussion about the kind of supervision the students would receive, the acting out of patients, transportation, the school's responsibility to the children and parents as well as the responsibility of the hospital to all concerned. This group suggested that the program be discussed at a student council meeting, with arrangements made beforehand by the principal.

At the meeting were representative students from the four classes. They were told about the Bedford Hospital located nine miles from Arlington which had fifteen hundred mental patients, of whom eighty were female, that about half were over sixty years of age, had been hospitalized for over ten years and had few visitors. They were given a verbal picture of the lonely life of these patients, their loss of interest in the outside world, and their feeling of hopelessness, despite excellent facilities provided by the government. What the patients need and respond to, they were told, was individual interest and understanding. Yes, they had all the advantages of a modern psychiatric hospital, new drugs, professional staff, but *that was not enough*. Individual attention, especially by younger people, would be helpful. It was suggested that these older patients were really not too different from older people that the children saw in their families or among their own friends.

The youth volunteers would be supervised either by staff of the hospital or an experienced adult volunteer in services to which they would be assigned. These included the clinical and research laboratories, dental service, dietetic service, manual arts therapy, nursing service, escort service, pharmacy, photo laboratory, print shop, educational therapy, occupational therapy, recreation, and the social work service. After much interesting discussion, the students asked to visit the hospital. This was arranged, with the principal and two guidance teachers accompanying twenty-five students.

At the hospital, the students were introduced to the assistant director of volunteer services and director of the youth volunteer program. The visit was planned to allow the young people to view a modern psychiatric hospital, to talk with the patients in the various clinics, and to meet supervisors in areas where they might be assigned. Subsequently, two additional discussion sessions were held at the high school. It became evident to school officials that the number of interested students far exceeded the original goal of ten.

DEVELOPMENT OF PROGRAM WITHIN THE HOSPITAL SETTING

Because of his personal conviction about the value of youth volunteers in our hospital, when the number of students finally approved was thirty, the hospital director made government transportation available. He discussed the program at top level meetings within the hospital. He pointed out the advantages of helping the community learn more about mental hospitals and mental illness, especially because the increasing number of patients returning to the community would require an understanding citizenry. Since our hospital has over two hundred and fifty different occupation categories, *career selection* would be of value to the students. Departments of the hospital held meetings with the youth volunteer program director to discuss areas for this youth activity. The program was described to staff members primarily as an *educational program* requiring investment of time, planning, and supervision.

Services given by the volunteers would be a by-product and would be the means through which the *educational process* would be stimulated. Opportunities to observe hospital areas other than those assigned would be made available.

SELECTION OF YOUTH VOLUNTEERS

In the selection of youth volunteers, the school guidance department and the principal had full responsibility. The hospital set as minimum requirements: age, fifteen years; sophomore year in high school; written parental permission. It is of interest to note that thirty students were approved by the school, and the parents of each gave permission. Factors contributing to such positive action may be due to the span of time allowed for discussion with the superintendent, the principal and other school officials (seven months), with the students (four months), and with the chief social worker's activity in Arlington where she has resided for the past twenty-one years.

PLAN OF PROGRAM AND ORIENTATION

The Bedford Hospital bus called for the children at 2:00 P.M. on Wednesdays at the high school where they were released from classes thirty minutes earlier than the other students. The director of the program accompanied them on their first few trips so that she could answer their many questions and become acquainted with them. Before individual assignments were made, according to interests of the youth volunteers, three sessions were devoted to an orientation to the hospital. The hospital director met with them and helped them see how important they were to the total treatment program and how each of them would benefit personally from the opportunities afforded by serving. The director of the volunteer service spoke about the entire volunteer program and where they fitted into the picture. The chief of social work helped them see the mental hospital as a community resource for the care of a particular illness, mental illness, stressing the opportunity of giving of themselves, of learning about mental hospitals and mental illness, and about career finding. At the third session, a film about volunteers was shown which the director of the program discussed in terms of their own feelings and attitudes. They were then sent to the supervisor of the area to which each was assigned.

PROGRAM WITHIN THE HOSPITAL

At the fourth session and every week thereafter the supervisors met the youths at the room where they all convened and each supervisor took his volunteer to his particular assignment and returned him at 4:15 P.M. so that all could leave in the bus before 4:30 P.M.

What did the students do? They worked in all areas mentioned in the early part of this chapter. In educational therapy, a youth volunteer helped one patient with his algebra, a requirement for the patient's high school diploma. The patient came regularly and worked on his assignments, something he had never done before. Another helped a patient with his French. In the social work service with geriatric patients, the volunteers gave supplemental nourishment. The amount of nourishment doubled when the attractive young volunteers offered it to the patients. They also played cards, checkers, and bowled. They each had particular patients to talk to or play cards with. In the escort service, the youth volunteers accompanied patients to various clinics. So many times before patients had refused to go. Now they enjoyed being accompanied by the young people. In the clinical and research laboratories the volunteers learned practical application of the chemistry and physics they were taking at school. The youth volunteers who assisted in the photo lab worked with employees and patients. In whatever area the youth volunteers were assigned, they became the focus of interest for patients as well as employees. They brought "sunshine" from the community into the hospital.

SUPERVISION

The supervision was constant and continuous. The director of the program greeted the students and saw them off. During their assignment, she made rounds at the various points of activity. She held meetings with the supervisors to keep in focus our educational goal, to iron out our problems, and to keep all informed of the progress of the program. The chief of social work became consultant to the program. Reports were made at top level management meetings so that all hospital personnel became better informed.

Giving full recognition to their unusual achievement in this pilot program, a "splash party" was held in May, 1962, after a scheduled session. Those who had completed twenty-five hours were awarded bar pins. A meal was served which had been selected by the volunteers in dietetics; pictures were taken by the youth volunteers in the photo lab. From all the discussion at the party, it was evident that the youth volunteers were comfortable in the hospital situation, and were gratified by their experiences.

EVALUATION OF YOUTH VOLUNTEER PROGRAM

At their last session, the students wrote an evaluation of their experience. The following are some excerpts:

"Hospital experience helped me shake some foolish ideas I had about mental illness." "Learned about life, people, and the ways in which they worked together." "My experience changed my ideas about mental hospitals and I told others about this." "Have a different concept of what a mental hospital is." "This accomplished a great deal for me, mostly spiritual."

The thread through all their reports showed that they had developed a tolerance for and acceptance of the mentally ill, and that they became sympathetic toward them. One student whose aunt had returned from a mental hospital became the spokesman for the family in talking with this aunt. Another reported that his father, recently discharged from a mental hospital, felt the family treated him with greater understanding after the youth began coming to Bedford.

The students' positive response to the experience was demonstrated by their high attendance record. The same group of thirty started and completed the year. There were no parental complaints to the school. Upon returning home after each session at Bedford, the volunteers discussed their activities with their parents and with their friends. Information about the mental hospital spread to their classmates and to anyone who would listen.

For the patients it was a heartwarming experience to look forward to the weekly visits of girls and boys who came to Bedford because they wanted to, and continued to come because they became interested in the patients as individual human beings. When the volunteers were absent because of illness or an exam, the patients wanted to know the reason and were most appropriate in their reactions. It was interesting to see patients not oriented to time and place knowing somehow the day that their youth volunteer would be coming and meeting them at the door.

Patients not personally involved with the volunteers met the bus to greet the young people, and saw them off, sometimes giving them a bar of candy or a flower. Attendance at the patients' library increased threefold with assignment of youth volunteers. One patient who always spoke symbolically told a youth volunteer that she wore the prettiest skirt he had ever seen.

At the June, 1962, meeting of the Veterans Administration Volunteer Association composed of forty voluntary groups that provide adult volunteers for the hospital, the program was devoted to "Youth Volunteers." The high school principal told of the advantages of this program which made full use of the energies and interest of the students. Four students conducted a panel discussion of their experiences. One said:

> Why did I volunteer at Bedford? I was curious. . . . I was scared. I didn't know what to expect even though I listened to all of the discussions. Once I got there I saw people who were not so different from many I see in Arlington. I wondered why these people were here. The kids at school asked me why I continued coming now that I saw the place and it wasn't so bad. I told them the patients looked forward to my visits. I felt needed and wanted, and I like being with them.

It is a tribute to the understanding of parents that the program continued and was a success. On Hospital Day, several of the students brought their parents and showed them around. Some served as guides for other visitors, assisted in serving punch, took pictures, answered questions, and talked of "our hospital." Several graduating seniors said that they would continue to volunteer at mental hospitals near their colleges.

The hospital considered this program one of the most worthwhile ventures it had participated in. The students' changing attitudes toward mental hospitals and mental illness were evident to staff. Personnel involved directly with the program were gratified in working with the young people who took their assignments seriously and with enthusiasm. Several personnel wanted their own children to participate in the program.

EXPANSION OF PROGRAM

The success of this pilot program brought about an expansion during the school year 1962-1963. Different sponsoring community agencies participated, always in cooperation with the school department and the hospital. High schools nearer to the hospital became involved. The Bedford High School with cooperation of the Red Cross and Hanscom Air Base sponsored twenty-seven students; the Andover High School through the Red Cross sponsored twelve; Lexington High School through the Lexington Mental Health Association sponsored thirty-seven; the Winchester Mental Health Association sponsored twenty; in addition, thirty-seven from the Arlington High School were sponsored by the Arlington Mental Health Association.

Arlington, Bedford, Lexington, and Winchester continued their interest in this program through the years with about one hundred participating each school year. The same number will participate for the year 1965-66. Transportation at times is still a problem but this has been solved because parents want their children to have this opportunity.

Of particular interest has been the developing use of these volunteers during the summer. Fifteen high school students participated during the summer of 1965, eight of whom had been volunteers during the winter. They came five days a week over a seven week period.

Comments from the youth volunteers through the years have been as follows: "I got more than I gave. It is much better than I expected. There is nothing to be afraid of there. The staff are so helpful. Now I know what I want to do."

That the volunteer experience contributed in their career decision-making is apparent from many reports received. A volunteer who was interested in photography pursued that while at Bedford. Today he is a commercial photographer. Three have gone to medical school, one to a school of dentistry, one has gone into the ministry, and several have gone to schools of pharmacy. A few have said, "I want to teach but not in a hospital." Others have pursued a career in teaching the handicapped. A project now in the early stages of development will assess the relationship between the volunteers' hospital experience and their subsequent career.

The potential of this program is viewed by the authors as far reaching. It is dependent upon several factors which have been mentioned already but bear repetition. To develop a youth volunteer program in a mental hospital, the community agency must be interested and ready to participate. The school must have an understanding of the mental hospital program and have confidence in its leadership. Sufficient time must be spent by the hospital staff in working with the sponsoring community agencies, parents, and the youth, to work through questions and problems. *Transportation is an important issue which must be dealt with realistically.*

The hospital staff must be given sufficient time to understand and plan for the program, and there must be full approval for this activity by top management. Continuous supervision must be provided. Careful selection of the students by the school is of primary importance. Complete acceptance of the program by parents is a requisite. Discussion of the program with patients on wards, buildings, and services where the youth volunteers are to be assigned must be carried on over a period of time so that the experience may be educational for the students and therapeutic for the patients.

The development and implementation of our national mental health program will require the cooperation of everybody in this country. As a result of their experiences at Bedford, our youth volunteers, their families, and friends will be better able to assume their responsibility in carrying out this program.

Chapter 19

RECRUITING FOR MENTAL HEALTH WORK: REPORT OF A PROGRAM WITH HIGH SCHOOL STUDENTS

PATRICIA L. EWALT*

LIBBIE B. BOWER, Ph.D.†

INTRODUCTION

The Mental Health Careers Program of the Massachusetts Association for Mental Health is a statewide educational and recruitment program functioning throughout the school year. It consists of apprentice work in mental institutions and state schools, mental health clubs in high schools, and related programs for students, parents and guidance counselors.

The program is based on an arrangement among high schools, mental institutions, and local mental health associations, facilitated by the state association. Its purposes are (1) to enlarge the number of students entering mental health occupations; (2) to increase participants' understanding of human behavior and (3) to interest students, parents, guidance counselors, and community leaders in mental health problems and training.

PROCEDURE

The program's plan is based on three observations in regard to volunteer service: (1) individuals who participate in mental health work often seem to improve their understanding of mental health

*Demonstration Officer
Massachusetts Mental Health Center
74 Fenwood Road
Boston, Mass.

†Consultant
Massachusetts Association for Mental Health, Inc.
38 Chauncy Street
Boston, Mass.

problems; (2) young people who participate in mental health work are sometimes encouraged to enter this field;[1] (3) the quality of supervision received by volunteers seems to affect their subsequent interest in mental health problems.[2]

The plan calls for a year-long apprentice program, carefully supervised by individual assignments to hospital staff members and by group discussions. Selection of students, hospital assignments, and community programs are carried out by a social worker (sometimes a psychologist or a psychiatric nurse); group supervision is provided by a psychiatrist, psychologist, or other person trained in group process. The educational aspects of talking *with* patients are explicitly emphasized, with consequent reduction in emphasis on service *to* patients.

The plan is flexible, permitting adaptation in any town with a high school, a mental health association (or an association for the retarded), and a hospital or clinic within commuting distance.

A pilot program was carried out during the school year 1962-1963 at the Massachusetts Mental Health Center, involving three local mental health associations and three high schools in different sections of greater Boston. Fifteen students participated. A mental health club was established by one of the local associations. The program has subsequently been extended throughout Massachusetts. Current enrollment is one hundred and forty students at nine institutions. Thirty high schools have cooperated together with eleven local associations.

Details of the program's functioning are not given here since they have been published with respect to the hospital[3,4] and to the club activities.[5] This chapter will be concerned with effects of the

---

[1] Kantor, D.: *Inducing Preferences for Mental Health Careers.* New York, N.A.S.W. 3092/75/5, 1957.

[2] Preliminary follow-up studies of the Harvard-Radcliffe Volunteer Program by Doctor Helen Reinherz were beginning to demonstrate this result. Her findings are discussed elsewhere in this volume and recorded in an unpublished doctoral dissertation, Harvard School of Public Health, April, 1965.

[3] Ewalt, P.L.: Massachusetts introduces students to mental health careers. *Ment Hosp, 16*:212-213, 1965.

[4] Ewalt, P.L.: Careers in Mental Health Program. Boston, Massachusetts Association for Mental Health, Inc. June, 1965.

[5] Ewalt, P.L.: Mental health club programs. *Ment Hyg, 49*:518-519, 1965.

apprentice experience upon participating students and upon the community.

STUDENT SELECTION AND ASSIGNMENT

Applicants from cooperating high schools are interviewed individually by the program supervisor. As a rule, fifteen students are selected from three or four high schools for the apprentice group at each institution. Students who are not selected may then be included in mental health clubs which provide service and educational opportunities in the community.

Students who are selected attend the hospital program one afternoon each week throughout the school year. They are assigned individually to professional staff on the wards: nurses, occupational therapists, social workers, psychiatrists, psychologists, chaplains, rehabilitation counselors or attendants. These preceptors pursue their usual activities as students talk or work with patients; at times the student joins an activity led by his staff person. After several weeks the student is reassigned to a member of a different profession.

When a student goes to the ward, there is no specific task for him to perform nor any specific patient for him to talk with. Our expectation is that students *will* talk with patients, and that through supervision, they will understand something of their own and patients' behavior when they do so. We are not interested in their learning details of mental pathology; we *are* interested in their growing perception of interpersonal relationships.

The ward assignment is followed each week by group discussion under direction of a leader who remains with the group throughout the year. In the group, students are encouraged to report their experience and observations carefully. Eventually, with support and tolerance, they become sensitive to the many levels of their interaction with patients. They can express their feelings and discuss them.

With professional leadership, students can progress from technical questions about mental illness, which tend to make a comfortable distinction between themselves and the mentally ill, to a broader consideration of human behavior.

Through examination of their own and patients' responses in the group meetings, students perceive that their behavior as well as that of patients has history and significance, that it can be understood and modified.

In our opinion, this insight into the meaningful nature of interaction is more important than anything else we have to teach about mental health work. It is a window to the mental health professions and, as students later report, has continuing importance in their personal lives.

We believe that the program's favorable effects may be attributed, to an important degree, to the relatively mature understanding achieved by students in the group meetings. We suspect that this procedure of group supervision for greater insight during a new and stressful experience may have application in programs outside the mental health field, for example, with neighborhood youth corpsmen and other economic opportunity groups.

FOLLOW-UP

We investigated two aspects of the program's influence on students: (1) influence on self-understanding and interpersonal relationships, and (2) influence on career choice.

A follow-up questionnaire is sent nine months after the conclusion of the program each year. Thus far, information has been sought from eighty students who participated during the pilot or the second year. Thirty-nine replies were received, representing programs at five institutions.

Since we now have more than one hundred participants each year as well as a larger number of applicants who cannot be accepted, we hope in time to acquire more conclusive indication of the program's vocational and other effects. We shall here report results which we have been able to observe thus far.

EFFECTS ON PERSONAL RELATIONSHIPS

Students were asked whether they thought their outlook or personal relationships had changed in a way related specifically to the careers program.[6] Many students attributed marked changes

---

[6] The follow-up questionnaire was prepared in collaboration with Daniel J. Levinson, Ph.D., Director, Center for Sociopsychological Research, Massachusetts Mental Health Center.

in attitude and relationships to this experience. These subjective observations were very often reiterated by guidance counselors.

Some students emphasized changes in attitude toward other persons:

> I have found an understanding for other people, and the need to often sympathize instead of rashly becoming angered with some of their annoying actions.

> Just understanding my two roommates' problems and their thinking, without condemning their actions, seemed to stem from a conscious effort on my part to learn about the cause and effect of relationships.

> I feel that the biggest change in me has been in my attitude towards people with emotional problems. I can't tell you what a difference that has made.

Other students (in spite of being selected as stable individuals) felt that they had derived a more comfortable feeling about themselves:

> I think what the program did was to show me that my problems, both family and social, are not unique and in most cases not as bad as I build them up to be. In a way it helped to settle me down and to think rationally about my problems.

From these and many similar responses, we believe that students do acquire an understanding of human behavior which they can apply in their subsequent relationships.

EFFECTS IN CAREER CHOICE

All students who apply are not necessarily interested in a mental health profession. Some wish to test related but nonpsychiatric interests such as medicine, nursing, speech therapy, or teaching. A number of students do not mention mental health among their career choices. Of one hundred and twenty students selected for whom we have record of initial preference, 18 per cent said they were not planning on mental health careers, 73 per cent said they were considering mental health, 9 per cent said they were intent on a mental health career.

Among students who responded, the number definitely preferring mental health work had increased from seven to sixteen. The number still undecided was fifteen as compared with an initial seventeen. The number preferring other work had decreased from fifteen to eight. (Most students who responded had originally stated a *definite* preference, in or *outside* mental health; most of those who did not answer had originally said they were undecided.)

The increment in the number definitely preferring mental health work was derived equally from the group which had been considering mental health and the group which had been thinking of different work.

Some preferences changed from nonpsychiatric scientific work to mental health:

> Before participating in this program I wasn't even thinking about a mental health career. My career was just going to be medicine. Now, through this program, I have decided to enter the field of psychiatry.

Some shifted from an unrelated field. This boy, although not an outstanding student, was selected because in interviewing him the supervisor was impressed by his interest in customers he met during his after school job as a clerk:

> When I entered the program in my senior year I had no idea of what I wanted to be. . . . I had thought of a number of fields but none seemed to satisfy me. After seeing the work of the social worker and his usefulness and the satisfaction he gains out of the job, I made up my mind to try to become a social worker. If it wasn't for the program I would have never even thought of looking into that field of work.

The principal of this boy's school reported that the program had a striking effect on his achievement. In spite of financial problems, he is now, two years later, persisting in his intentions to become a social worker.

Other students who had been considering mental health confirmed their preference:

> The careers program certainly influenced my choice. I had always been interested in psychology but looked upon it as some vague rosy career in which troubled broken people would receive my magic care and leave healthy and normal. I saw what really goes on at a mental hospital. Nothing was hidden from us or

glossed over. My vague career is no longer vague; I know what I want to do and next year at college I plan to start right in with psych. courses. I know what I'm working toward and I'm eager to start working.

Two persons decided not to pursue a mental health career. Each said she had realized her earlier interest stemmed from family problems rather than a lasting career interest. This realization was, in our opinion, a gain for these students.

RESULTS AMONG FACULTY AND FELLOW STUDENTS

This program required a working relationship among mental health associations, high schools and mental institutions. We feel that the effort involved in establishing this relationship is well worthwhile.

Guidance counselors reported that widespread interest in mental health was evoked in the schools. They particularly appreciated the careful supervision which was a part of this vocational testing experience:

> The motivation provided by the project was not limited to the five girls who participated—their enthusiasm affected the whole school.
>
> I feel that the effects are far reaching, not only will it encourage future careers but it tends to help educate many others.

Nearly all of the counselors asked if we could possibly accommodate more of their students. Through their interest we were requested to describe the program at a New England Regional Guidance Conference.

A student reported similar widespread interest among fellow students:

> We held a panel discussion at the high school near the end of the program and I was surprised at the number of students who attended, the interest they showed, and mainly the variety they represented.

We believe that the response among students makes an impression upon the faculty, parents and the wider community:

> I think this program did have a definite effect on both the students and staff of my high school. I think the fact that all of

us students kept it up for the entire year with very few absences and so much enthusiasm gave them a new outlook. I would also like to say, that I think that the program had an effect on our parents and other area people who heard or read about it.

Five who are seniors in Leominster High this year composed a stirring letter to the Mayor in support of public health appropriation for our clinic . . . many people feel that it contributed substantially to pressure which kept the issue open . . . We are terribly proud that the mental health awareness of these students continues to find expression.

Perhaps the most concrete indications of results are increased time and money given by the participating partners.

Originally the state association secured grants from foundations for nearly all expenses.[7] During the past two years, local associations, even those with very small budgets, have begun to share the cost. The state association has assigned a staff person to work on this program.

Most hospitals have increased the number of students they are willing to accept. More hospital staff are assisting within the hospital and in the community. With the Neighborhood Youth Corps, the plan is being adapted to interest suitable young people to train for ancillary occupations.

Two state school parents' associations have begun to provide four-year scholarships for outstanding program graduates who wish to become special class teachers.

A bill is now before the state legislature, with the Commissioner's recommendation, to give official standing to this program within the Department of Mental Health.

SUMMARY

The Massachusetts Association for Mental Health has found that the Mental Health Careers Program is an agent to engage the cooperation of high schools, hospitals, and local mental health associa-

---

[7] This program has been made possible by grants from the Maurice Falk Medical Fund, Pittsburgh; Permanent Charity Fund, Boston; Charles H. Hood Dairy Foundation; Hoffman-LaRoche Laboratories; Fortnightly Club, Sharon; Massachusetts Federation of Women's Clubs; together with support of cooperating mental health associations and parents' groups of Wrentham and the Paul A. Dever Schools for the retarded.

tions. The program has found wide acceptance among these organizations; each organization finds the program conducive to accomplishing its goals.

Students who have participated report a broader understanding of human behavior, including that of the mentally ill. A number of students have been confirmed in their choice of a mental health profession and others have become committed to this choice through their experience in the program.

Chapter 20

THE HUMAN RELATIONS LABORATORY: A COLLEGE MENTAL HEALTH CAREERS PROGRAM

IRVING SANDERS, M.A.*

PRESTON DAVIS, Ph.D.†

T HE COLLEGE Mental Health Careers Program which we call the Human Relations Laboratory represents a working partnership between two mental health associations and a state hospital with the assistance of ten colleges. It differs from many other programs in that it is a structured, career-oriented, not volunteer-oriented program, yet it combines many of the best features of a youth volunteer program, a public education program, and a program for recruitment to mental health careers.[1]

It exemplifies the most effective kind of cooperation between mental health associations and mental hospitals and indicates the effectiveness to which such cooperation can lead in a teaching program. It provides the possibility of an accurate estimate of the effect of the program in terms of recruitment for mental health careers.

Our college program grew out of a mental health careers committee formed in 1961, comprised of the Norfolk and South Shore Mental Health Associations in Massachusetts. This committee co-sponsored several large one-day institutes, some for high school students and others for superintendents, high school principals,

---

*See Chapter 16, page 104 for Irving Sander's address.

†Chief Psychologist
 Medfield State Hospital
 Harding, Mass.

[1] The authors wish to acknowledge the volunteer leadership provided this project by Mrs. William Weisman, Careers Chairman of the Norfolk Mental Health Association, Inc.

guidance counselors and other personnel in a position to influence students in their career choices.

In the spring of 1964, we sponsored a one-day institute at Medfield State Hospital attended by one hundred and seventy students from twelve colleges. Six months later, the fall semester of the Human Relations Laboratory was launched, meeting for three hours one day a week. Seventy students from nine colleges participated in this program. The first hour was didactic, with lectures on mental health principles by both intra- and extra-mural mental health personnel; the second hour consisted of one-to-one student-patient contact in a hospital work setting; the third hour consisted of small-group discussions led by trained professional persons. This program continued from September to late December.

In the spring of 1965, an advanced, more intensive course was offered for twenty carefully selected students. This program took the form of team projects involving four or five students supervised by experienced professional persons. The students utilized data acquired during clinical contacts with patients as a basis for pure and applied research. Results of these studies were presented in a number of papers including: "Readiness of Young Patients for Continued Schooling," "Correlates of Performance in a Sheltered Workshop," and "Admissions to State Hospitals by Days of the Week."

What was our rationale for embarking on a careers program for college students? We had already attracted some two hundred high schoolers as well as one hundred of their guidance counselors and school administrators to one-day institutes. Those who served on the steering committee suspected that another large group of students, nearer to making their vocational commitments, was untapped by any existing recruitment program. Because they are closer to entering vocations, it seemed that a careers program geared to the college student might bear fruit more rapidly.

Those who work with teenagers know that a characteristic feature is their frequent change in attitudes toward life goals. Who knows whether a youngster influenced favorably toward a mental health career as a high school senior may change his mind before he is ready to embark on his ultimate vocational choice? We felt that because so many reach their junior or senior year in college without making firm vocational choices, it was important to develop a program to reach the college student. This feeling was also communicated to us in interviews with many college educators.

Let us cite the unique characteristics of this program which we feel could be profitably undertaken by other mental health associations:

1. Cooperative sponsorship characterized this program. Two mental health associations, a state hospital, ten colleges and four small charitable foundations cooperated in this ongoing program.

2. The ten participating colleges included a diversity of institutions: junior and senior colleges, co-ed and single-sex colleges, church-related and nondenominational colleges, all working together in a single program. Students from all colleges were integrated in this program. Faculty from all participated jointly.

3. College faculty were drawn in early to help plan and evaluate the program as it proceeded. We established a faculty seminar which has met before, during and after each program. As many as twenty faculty persons have participated in these sessions. Several faculty members took the entire course themselves.

4. Since we worked with ten colleges, we were obliged to find the *common denominator* of their academic needs.

5. We offered substantial course content. Our program was carefully planned by the committee and was administered by a psychologist with a Ph.D. on the hospital staff. Most of the participating schools offered course credit despite the various administrative hurdles encountered in doing so. We developed a grading system which determined eligibility for the advanced course and provided a basis for colleges to grade the students. The spring program was planned to acquaint students with the problems of research at both the theoretical and practical levels.

6. The entire careers program is headed by a volunteer who is a director of one of the sponsoring mental health associations and who has invested much time and effort in the program.

7. We exposed students to the entire hospital structure. Our program has reached not only the clinical departments but has involved lively participation by the business and maintenance departments of the hospital.

8. Although our underlying aim was to promote mental health

careers, our method was to offer a close-up view of mental health
workers and a mental health facility. Students were permitted
to perceive needs and opportunities for themselves with occasional reminders that they might consider careers in this field.
9. Student-patient contacts were made, not in the motionless
backwater of a ward visiting room, but at job locations in the
laundry, kitchen, farm, housekeeping assignments or sheltered
workshop. An important by-product of this type of contact was
the noticeable moving together of the clinical-educational and
the industrial divisions of the hospital. We had full cooperation
of the top echelon of the hospital throughout the program. The
assistant superintendent was an active member of our committee.
10. In our spring program we sought to offer as much latitude
for student creativity as we could.

We are now in the middle of the autumn, 1965, phase of this
program. As the Human Relations Laboratory enters its second
full academic year, we perceive its functions as follows:
1. To offer a first-rate field experience in a mental health
facility to colleges in and near the Medfield-Norfolk-South Shore
area.
2. To encourage students' consideration of the mental health
field as their vocational choice.
3. To examine experimentally the relationship among the following: the degree of autonomy or self-structuring offered to
students in their activities relating to patients; the creative effort
that students exert in those activities; changes in patients' behavior and changes in attitudes of students toward mental illness.

We find that we are in an especially favorable position for
undertaking research on some aspects of the educational process
at the college level. Our student body represents a sample of a
number of colleges of different types; hence we can assume findings
to be fairly representative of colleges in general. Students come to
the program with positive attitudes, with the expectation of finding
an enriching experience. By allowing for different kinds and degrees
of creativeness and then observing the variations in these attitudes
and in other measures, we hope to move closer to an understanding
of: (1) creativeness in the educational process; (2) the creative
commitment to a career field.

A two-year program to this end was mapped out in the summer of 1965. The current program is serving as a tryout period, with considerable time being devoted to the collection and analysis of tests and other data. There are three treatments of students in terms of guidance and supervision of their patient contacts. These allow or encourage varying degrees of autonomy and creativeness.

Teams of three students meet every week with groups of five patients. Maximum autonomy and chance for creativeness is offered those teams assigned to the *free-choice* treatment. Students are largely on their own to formulate methods of working with their patient groups. *Discussion* teams are given weekly topics which serve as a starting point, but relative freedom is afforded as to the way in which the topics may be handled. Students who use the *remotivation* technique have rather precise methods of procedure laid out for them. They can exercise creativity of a kind, but their available methods are limited.

We predict that all three experimental groups will gain more positive and liberal attitudes on mental health topics than will comparable students who have not attended the course. We also predict that differences in these changes of attitude will be detectable among our three experimental treatments: greater autonomy is expected to lead to greater gain in positive attitudes.

This study of autonomy and attitude change, as indicated, is currently at the pilot or tryout stage. Data will be computer-analyzed and a more formal study will be run in the autumn of 1966. The findings, we hope, will include implications for creativity in the educational process, as well as for mental health education and career commitment.

The spring programs enroll a smaller number of students (about thirty) and afford little opportunity for testing of the students. Rather, supervisors of student groups try to encourage students to get the *feel* of the creative process.

A possibility being considered for 1967 is collaboration with the Cushing Hospital, a geriatric facility, in research on students' attitudes toward aging. Our current testing instruments bear on these attitudes, since the students' group contacts are with older patients.

In common with other observers of college students in a mental hospital setting, we have noted remarkable enthusiasm, resiliency, and creativeness among these young people. They continue to work with the mute or hostile patient long after we expect them to give up. When allowed to define and plan their own work, to be as creative as possible, they invest many more hours than we expect. Career commitments, we think, tend to stem from this kind of investment.

In order to determine at what age level mental health careers should be introduced and what kinds of educational programming are most effective, a large longitudinal research study of thousands of students might be necessary. Since this is beyond our resources to undertake, we think that the kind of college program in which we have been involved is well worth doing in other mental hospitals around the country. We believe that there is nothing we have done which cannot be done elsewhere.

As a recruiting effort for the mental health field, as a contribution to human relations education in a number of colleges, and as a source of valuable research, the Human Relations Laboratory can provide a model for college mental health careers programming by other mental health associations.

PART V

**VOLUNTEERISM AND PROBLEMS OF DOMAIN IN THE
AMERICAN MENTAL HEALTH MOVEMENT**

Chapter 21

VOLUNTEERISM AND PROBLEMS OF DOMAIN IN THE AMERICAN MENTAL HEALTH MOVEMENT

DAVID KANTOR, Ph.D.*

VOLUNTEERISM as an American characteristic cannot be separated from other aspects of American culture. Volunteerism shares a vitality with literature, art, music, dance, the theatre, and architecture, although until now it has lacked the visibility of these other cultural phenomena. Outsiders like de Tocqueville who have scanned the American scene, have been struck by this aspect of the American imagination. However, not until the establishment of the foreign Peace Corps by the federal government did volunteering achieve visibility among nonvolunteers on the home shores.

It is easy to overlook the fact that at the root of volunteerism in America is a frustration produced by the disparity between what people have come to expect and what in reality exists. Americans believe that almost anything can be accomplished, that few things can't be changed. We hold that every problem has its solution, every malady its cure, every villain a conquering hero. The success of the American experiment on the whole justifies this optimism. The free enterprise system and the industrial revolution have spread the wealth over a fairly broad base of the population. A remarkably stable political system has established a set of rights and freedoms that remains a model of conception even when it fails in application. When these failures occur, they are reminders that the system is imperfect after all; they disturb the structure of the American dream.

*Special Fellow, National Institute of Mental Health
Boston State Hospital
591 Morton Street
Boston

It is not, however, by frustration that the American people do something about deprivations of less fortunate persons, but by mechanisms to convert frustration into constructive action. Acts of volunteerism, then, are likely to flourish when there are able persons convinced that *their* actions can benefit the lives of others and bring them nearer to the "good life," as culturally prescribed. This increased interest can best be understood in the light of trends that have taken place in the mental health movement, and changes that have taken place generally in our national culture.

In America, Great Britain, and some European countries, the social sciences are having a tremendous impact upon the institutional apparatus which ministers to the needs of emotionally disturbed people. Treatment of the mental patient, once thought to be strictly the province of medicine, has been extended recently to psychologists, social workers, ministers, and, at times, to volunteers. Until recently, the psychiatrist's office and the mental hospital were held up as the best, if not the only, legitimate arrangement for handling the mentally ill. Such a view is untenable today in the climate created by reformers who have expanded the structures for affecting mental illness.

Indeed, many of our once-precious traditions are now open to question and criticism. Coming under scrutiny is the legacy of "custodial care," a monument of the late nineteenth century created for patients with the greatest social deficits and the smallest political voice. Also under examination is the exclusive arrangement between psychiatric specialists and the comparatively small number of individuals endowed with "treatable" symptoms and with motivation and money to do something about them. These policies, of *defeatism* with our "worst" patients and *elitism* with our "best" patients which went unchallenged in the past, are being reviewed in the 1960's. So strong is the force for change that new means for coping with the mentally ill are being developed at a pace never before equalled in this country.

One of these developments, the upsurge of citizen interest in the mentally ill, is decidedly among the important new factors affecting patient care in this country. Volunteerism is more than a cultural and moral force. It is an economically meaningful phenomenon. Its political significance is certain to increase as volunteer efforts are recognized as a social asset and a treatment tool.

Accurate figures do not exist on the number of volunteers working with the mentally ill. According to some published estimates, over sixty million people volunteered in 1960 in this country's health and welfare programs. There is no doubt that the mentally ill have not held their own in competition for America's voluntary financing and manpower. But mental illness has emerged since World War II to claim a substantial segment of the total volunteer resource.

This upsurge of citizen interest and activity in mental health represents a union of complexly related historical, social, and cultural forces, which I shall not attempt to describe in full. I would like to cite four developments which seem to have fostered the increase in mental health volunteerism.

1. First is a marked change in the people's response to mental patients and therefore in decision-making with respect to the mentally ill. This change is due in part to an evolution from an age of darkness to an age of enlightenment in society's view toward the mentally ill; in part, it is the result of persevering efforts among mental health workers, legislators, and other citizens to educate the public.

2. A second development affecting volunteerism is a radical change in our economy. Technological progress has succeeded so well that it has become necessary to restrict whole groups from participating in useful, gainful work. The chief examples are women, young people, and old people. Among these people are many who may be looking for a sphere for legitimate social action where they can feel "productive" and socially useful.

3. A third factor contributing to increased citizen interest reflects developments within the mental health field. In the 1950's, large public mental hopitals possessed a malaise which any astute observer could detect. Disenchantment was felt with the concept of helping the majority of psychotics in these hospitals through individual psychotherapy. The usual factors of insufficient staff and overcrowded, inadequate facilities called into question the policy fashionable at the time, that mental hospitalization was the preferred treatment for major mental illness.

The enigma of custodial hospitals attracted attention of social scientists, mental health workers, and citizen volunteers. All of them were seeking to liberate hospitalized patients from insulting social circumstances in programs whose achievements were exceedingly limited. In this climate, sentiment for a comprehensive program based solidly in the community ran high and amassed support. The energies of citizen volunteers were channeled first into hospital work and then, as community mental health picked up steam, into community aftercare programs where volunteers are now making some of their most creative contributions.

4. Fourth, and finally, is a notable uprating of the "volunteer role." Today the idea of untrained citizens working in the service of community and society is accorded higher value and prestige than ever before. This positive assessment is aided by Peace Corps work and civil rights work which have high visibility and government support. While the volunteer is still a second-rate citizen in the status hierarchy of health and welfare organizations, the professional staff and other paid officials of these organizations have acquired a clearer understanding of and respect for the contribution which volunteers can make toward *their* organizational goals. The idea that volunteers can offer a partial solution to some of the manpower problems of welfare operations has a certain functional appeal. Thus, an increase in the absolute functional value of volunteer work has tended to open an ever-widening channel of opportunities for voluntary service.

Until recently the question never came up as to whether our potential reservoir of trained personnel was going to prove adequate to a constantly growing demand. We sought comfort in what seems to have been an unrealistic faith that our manpower needs could be met through more effective methods of recruiting. We now know that despite all efforts to persuade men and women to enter service professions, the demand will continue to outrun the supply, and that manpower deficits will have to be made up from groups who never become part of the professional structure.

Volunteers may become one of the major resources in production of services for mental patients. Such a prospect is likely because in times of rapid social change, traditional limits are not rigidly observed and there is more willingness to experiment with new forms. It remains to be seen how volunteer movements will respond to the prevailing winds of change and opportunity.

A survey which I conducted by mail in 1963 forcefully shows that volunteers are pouring an extraordinary amount of energy, time and invention into their work with mental patients. There is immense variety in the aims and structures of programs, in the roles assumed by volunteers, and in the sponsoring arrangements. This investigation showed that on the whole the professional structure is glad to have volunteer participation and that professional staff and volunteers collaborate fruitfully in most programs.

However, there are also strains in the relations between trained personnel and untrained volunteers. I would like to examine this aspect of volunteer work for a few moments. Understandably it receives precious little public discussion. Those who oppose the incursions of volunteers in mental health realms and those who advocate giving volunteers broader scope and more responsibility have been politely quiet about any troubles occurring as they work together.

Because most professional persons believe that nonexperts have something valuable to contribute, that they can help to achieve the ideal of bringing services to everyone, not merely to the solvent or the sophisticated or those in acute crisis, the system of relationships between these role partners needs to be examined.

The introduction of unpaid and so-called inexpert workers into domain traditionally occupied by salaried workers and specialists has resulted in frictions which I consider to be disputes over territory, jurisdiction, and sovereignty. These problems of domain are common whenever occupational groups feel that their rights or their boundaries are being threatened. Friction occurs when these groups take steps to protect themselves.

I have identified five typical situations in which conditions for conflict between expert and nonexpert servers are particularly ripe:[1]

1. Where the idea of bringing in volunteers is new or considered to be relatively radical in the local culture where it is being proposed:

Citation: A group of citizen volunteers in a western state

---

[1] Examples are drawn from the above-mentioned survey conducted by the author in 1963.

sought to assist patients returning from the state mental hospital to sparsely populated rural areas where rehabilitation services virtually did not exist. Powerful professional and citizen groups, fearing that some unnamed harm would come to the patients put in the "unskilled hands" of volunteers, campaigned subtly to abort the expected disaster, and the program, bogged down by systematic opposition, was terminated by the volunteers in despair and defeat.

2. Where the new class of servers enters the territory of expert servers whose authority and status is not firmly established, and who are therefore threatened by incursions from subordinate positions:

Citation: In a volunteer program with individual patients in a large state hospital, a social service staff, clearly insecure about its professional status, vehemently opposed the project and refused outright to refer prospective patients.

3. Where the new class of servers disregards the authority of established status groups and challenges existing regulative mechanisms with ideologies, methods and controls of its own design:

Citation: *Wellmet* is an unusual halfway house in which chronic patients and a group of undergraduate college students live together cooperatively in a family-like arrangement under provisions of an essentially democratic and open society. Experimenting with many new features of organization and practice, the program initially ran into strong resistance from institutional structures which would not integrate the house's function into established classifications and formulations, and challenged its right to exist.

4. Where the new class of servers interferes with mechanisms of the status quo *which are latently functional for important status groups in the systems they enter:*

Citation: A "back ward" for chronic schizophrenic patients was "invaded" by a swarm of enthusiastic volunteers whose vision was to activate patients, improve their physical environment, and give them human dignity. Expecting to form an alliance with attendants who complained of being overworked and as forgotten as the patients, volunteers instead locked horns with these ward personnel, fighting them at every turn for more human and more mature patient performance. At issue were the latent, unrecognized benefits which this so-called custodial system, and the attendants themselves, derived from preserving the *status quo* and keeping the system (its norms, its values, its goals) just as it was.

5. *When new territory is being charted by professional groups and new roles are being forged so that professional workers move into territory which nonprofessional status groups consider theirs:*

> *Citation*: As the concepts of social psychiatry and community mental health gain a more secure foothold in actual programs implemented in the community, organized citizen groups which have seen the "community" as their domain, will speak up for their rights and compete with professional groups for power in the new structures being created. In one Eastern city famous for decentralized local government, such a struggle is currently going on, though the parties are reluctant to face the issue as one of "territorialism."

While most salaried workers in mental health have welcomed volunteers into their camp enthusiastically or at least with a "let's wait and see" attitude, others have overtly or covertly opposed volunteers, using subtle resistance to slow down progress or levelling unwarranted and sometimes absurd attacks against them. Volunteers, say these detractors, may endanger the patient. They may leave themselves open to some kind of damage. Or volunteers are branded as "charlatans" or "curiosity hounds" who may exploit patients in some way. The most frequent charge is that they are moving into areas which require special knowledge or technical competence.

When these charges and arguments are clearly unfounded, to what may we attribute them? I cite these reasons, some food for thought:

1. Reactions to volunteers may mirror internal disputes and power struggles going on within the professional community itself.

2. Professional personnel who take it upon themselves to carry out their watchdogging functions with a vengeance may be covering up some of their own needs, for example the need to control patients.

3. Success by nonexperts in areas where trained workers have

admittedly failed or withdrawn their attention may arouse guilt and cause embarrassment.

4. Professionalism involves demonstrating a special competence that cannot reasonably be acquired by novices and untrained servers. Attacks on volunteers by professional workers may thus be an effort to make distinctions between the expert and nonexpert. The practice of separating by rank qualified from unqualified workers helps to establish the professional person's independence and to solemnize and dignify his role.

5. A prerogative which professional groups consider sacred is the right to privacy and self-regulation. While professionals are accountable to the community, they feel that details should not be subjected to too much scrutiny. Professions enjoy a high degree of self-control through codes of ethics operated by the specialists themselves. Volunteers, on the other hand, take seriously their citizen role as moral conscience for society and, in this context, feel that the scope and scale of professional activity should be subjected to scrutiny and public discussion.

I might say, *a propos* of this last point, that one of the real dangers that I see in bringing volunteers into the mental health structure is that they may find themselves so closely allied with professional and other paid workers and so well integrated into the service structure that the citizen community will lose some of its ability to function as an independent critic.

We have now seen that volunteers may meet some opposition from professional and salaried workers which they will have to work hard to overcome. My own view is that in such situations competition and conflict often have positive as well as negative functions. As volunteers work out difficulties due not only to professional resistance but also to their own bungling, as they forge legitimate roles for themselves, they will have to face internal issues inevitably arising in a growing organization.

Every organization, as it progresses from idea to institution, faces a host of difficult problems: what image to present to the public; how to recruit and train members; how to build an apparatus for effectively controlling members; how to acquire legitimate status without sacrificing autonomy; how to offer something special without "specializing" or becoming rigid; how to develop mechanisms for orderly transition of power and responsibility; how to reward loyalty, preserve morale, contain factionalism; how to preserve original ideals and aims; how to establish structures that permit change to take place.

It may be useful to restate a few of these issues briefly. There are three tendencies which volunteers may do well to check:

1. *Bureaucratization.* Volunteer progroms may be able to retain spontaneity and flexibility if they avoid the trap of developing along bureaucratic lines.

2. *Professionalism.* The value of the volunteer is in his uniqueness. There is a tendency in volunteer programs to become too preoccupied with training and supervision. The reasons for supervision are obvious; the failure to help volunteers perform adequately is clearly irresponsible. But there may be a trend toward too much control, and toward a professionalization which diminishes the volunteer's role.

3. *Rigidification.* Even a casual inspection of volunteer programs reveals that these organizations have a life of their own and are going through stages. Any organization, however idealistic, may degenerate in time, maintaining little of its original zeal. Volunteers could profitably consider what happens in the history of different kinds of organizations with a view to discovering how to stay alive organizationally.

Because very few organizational considerations are more important than how to recruit new members effectively, leaders of volunteer programs always raise questions about the "motivation" of volunteers, about "selection," and they talk a lot about "screening."

The motivation to "serve" is a complex and highly individualistic matter. In studies of volunteer motivation and style which I have done with Victor Gelineau,[2] it has not been possible to find a good predictor for successful performance. We have not found standard psychological tests and clinical assessments to be of much use. Pathology can be as functional and dysfunctional in volunteering as it is in other occupational groups.

Our studies reveal a variety of motivations among "good"

---

[2] This refers to a five-year study of college volunteers supported in part by P.H.S. Grant No. OM-233.

volunteers.

The wish to *escape* the routinization of life in family, school, or job; the chance to be among social peers, to join others in a worthwhile cause; the chance to actuate the service traditions of family or social class; a moral concern for the underdog who is suffering institutional wrongs: these are all "good" reasons for volunteering. They should not be judged in terms that presuppose, without empirical support, a hierarchy of values. There is a tendency to devalue some people's motives because they are personal; this can be extremely wasteful and it often tells us very little either about the behavior of the volunteer or the consequences which his behavior has for others.

It is presumptuous to presuppose that a recognized sense of social guilt is worth more or less than an unrecognized sense of personal guilt. The childless woman who volunteers seeking maternal fulfillment and the college student who is testing a service career are both role-playing. Who is to say, out of context, which is more functional for the patients they see?

I have dwelled upon the question of style and motivation because I consider it to be the most crucial of all, one which, in my judgement, we have repeatedly failed to appreciate. I am not against screening. My experience has been, however, that the really vital and dynamic programs, the ones that achieve their purposes and find new and better ones as they go along, are not the ones which devote themselves to "screening out" objectionable and disruptive types. The vital programs are those that keep places open for helpful critics of the *status quo,* individuals who tend naturally to work their way *out* of organizations which become too well-adjusted, static and ingrown.

INDEX

A

Acute patients, case aides with, 43
Advanced training, case aide, 43-44
Aftercare
  arranged by volunteers, 10, 11, 98, 102
  for patients in family care, 49
  in cooperative apartment program, 84-86, 88
Apartment, cooperative, 79-88
Apprentice, high school volunteer as, 130, 131
Attitudes, effect of supervision on, 114-115
  See also Community understanding
Attrition of clinic volunteers, 15

B

Businessmen
  as workshop sponsors, 73-74
  use skills to assist patients, 9-10
Boston State Hospital
  case aide program at, 35-44
  fashion therapy program at, 60-64
  sheltered workshop at, 73-76
  VISTA program at, 52-59
Brookline Assn. for Mental Health
  cooperative apartment of, 79-88
  paid employment workshop of, 65-72

C

Career choice, 39, 50, 127, 133-135
  effect of supervision on, 115-116
Careers program
  Human Relations Laboratory 138-143
  Mental Health Careers Program, 129-137
Case aide
  in Boston State Hospital Case Aide Program, 35-44

  in Mental Health Assn. Case Aide Program, 45-51
  See also subheadings
Center Club (for discharged patients), 89-94
  See also Torchlighters 95-98
Central Middlesex Mental Health Assn.
  case aide program, 45-51
Chronic patients
  case aide programs with, 35-44, 45-51
  college volunteers with, xi-xii, 142-143, 35-44, 111-119
  fashion therapy program with, 60-64
  high school volunteers with, 120-128
  social clubs for, 89-94, 95-98
  sheltered workshops for, 65-72, 73-76
VISTA volunteers with, 54-55, 56
Clarinda plan (unit system), 26
Clinic volunteer program, 12-17
College student volunteers, xi-xii, 14, 20, 30, 46
  follow-up study of, 111-119
  in careers program, 138-143
  in case aide program, 35-44
Commonwealth Service Corps, 18-22
Community aides, 10-11
  See also Social aides
Community group involvement in mental health programs, 5-6, 50-51, 100, 135-137
Community understanding increased by volunteering 6-7, 15-16, 50-51, 114, 125, 135-137
  See also Attitudes; Supervision
Contracts, sheltered workshop, 67, 68, 71, 74
Cooperative apartment, 79-88
Coordinator of VISTA program, 53-54, 56-57
  See also Supervisor
Costs, *See* Funding
Course material
  of college careers program, 139
  of fashion therapy program, 60-64

D

Direct service of volunteers, 7-14
Disputes, professional-volunteer, 151-153

E

Elderly as volunteers, 19-20, 38-40
  See also Retired professionals, 9-10
Employment
  assist patients in finding, 9,83, 98, 100-101, 106
  paid workshop, 65-72
Emergency care, in cooperative apartment, 85
  See also Aftercare

F

Family care placement by case aides, 49-50
  See also Home-finding, 37, 39
Fashion therapy program, 60-64
Financial assistance to patients, 83, 84, 87-88
Financial clinic as preventive service, 10
Financial support of volunteer programs, *See* Funding
Follow-up
  of college volunteers, 111-119
  of high school volunteers, 132-135
  See also Aftercare
Funding
  of case aide program, 46
  of college program, 140
  of Commonwealth Service Corps, 20
  of cooperative apartment, 81
  of high school program, 136
  of sheltered workshops, 67-68, 73-74
  of social clubs, 93-94, 96
Families of patients seen by volunteers, 7, 39-40, 50

G

General service volunteer, 7-8
Goals of volunteers, study of, 112-114
Greater Lawrence Guidance Center, volunteers in, 12-17
Group aides, 44
Group meetings in sheltered workshops, 70-75

Groups, community, *See* Community groups
Groups, supervisory
  of case aides, 36, 38, 40, 42, 47-48
  of high school volunteers, 131-132
  of VISTA volunteers, 57

H

Halfway house, *See* Cooperative apartment, 79-88
Harvard-Radcliffe student volunteers, xi-xii
  follow-up study of, 111-119
High school volunteers
  Mental Health Careers Programs, 129-137
  youth volunteer program, 120-128
Home-finding by case aides, 37, 39
  in family care homes, 49-50
Hospital volunteer programs, 25-31, 32-34
  See also subheadings
Human Relations Laboratory (college careers program), 138-143

I

Informal organization of hospital, 32-34
Intervener, 10
Indirect service volunteer, 7, 14

J

Jobs, *See* Employment
Joint planning of volunteer services, 99-101, 104-107

L

Language retraining by volunteers, 15
Leisure activity, importance of volunteering as, 6

M

Manpower, 41-42, 150-151
  See also Careers

Members, of social clubs, 89-90, 96
  See also Selection of patients
Mental health careers program, 129-137, 138-143
Mental health assn. case aide program, 45-51
Metropolitan State Hospital
  case aide program at, 45-51
  cooperative apartment for discharged patients of, 79-88
  follow-up of college volunteers at, 111-119
  paid employment workshop at, 65-72
Motivation of volunteers, 39, 50, 155-156
  See also Recruitment; Selection of volunteers

N

Norfolk Mental Health Assn., Inc.
  college careers program of, 138-143
  continuity in volunteer program of, 104-107

O

Occupational therapist, as supervisor of volunteers, 61, 63
Open ward, effect on volunteer program of, 29
Orientation of volunteers
  course for, 13, 15-16
  of Commonwealth Service Corps, 21
  of fashion therapy program, 62
  of high school volunteers, 123
  of VISTA volunteers, 53-54
  See also Training; Supervision
Opposition to volunteers, 151-154

P

Paid employment workshop, 65-72
Patients
  as volunteers, 29-30, 33
  expectations of hospitalized, 27
  represented in determining services, 19
  response to volunteer programs, 36-37, 39-40, 48-49, 62-64, 70-71, 76, 125-126
  See also Chronic patients; Selection of patients; subheadings

Payment
  of debts by patients, 84
  of patients in workshop, 67, 71
  of volunteers, 19-20
Placement of clinic volunteers, 16
Placement of patients in homes, 37, 39, 49-51
Preventive services by volunteers, 6, 10, 14, 43
Process of socialization in social club, 89-90
PROP sheltered workshop, 73-76
Psychiatrist, as group supervisor, 57, 130-132
Psychologist, as advisor of social club, 95-96

R

Recruitment
  of case aides, 38, 42, 47
  of case aide supervisors, 41
  of clinic volunteers, 14-15
  of Commonwealth Service Corpsmen, 19-20
  of social aides, 100, 106
  See also Careers; Manpower
Rehabilitation, *See* subheadings
Rehabilitation Commission (Massachusetts)
  in cooperative apartment, 80, 83-85
  in sheltered workshop, 65-72
Research
  on case aide program, 42
  on educational process, 141-143
  on professional supervision, 111-119
Retired professionals as volunteers, 9-10
  See also Elderly
Retraining, language, by volunteers, 15
Role clarification, of volunteers, 8

S

Selection of patients to be served
  in case aide programs, 37-38, 47-49
  in cooperative apartment, 82-83, 85-86, 87
  in fashion therapy program, 62
  in sheltered workshops, 69-71, 74
Selection of volunteers
  in case aide program, 47
  in clinic, 16

in Commonwealth Service Corps, 21
in fashion therapy program, 61-62
in high school programs, 123, 131
in hospitals, 29-30
in social clubs, 92, 96
See also Motivation; Recruitment
Sheltered workshop, 65-72, 73-76
Social Aide Organization, 99-103
Social aides, 99-103, 104-107
Social club, 95-98
See also Center Club
South Shore Mental Health Assn.,
careers program of, 138-143
Spokesmen, volunteers as, 6
Stability of volunteer programs related
to supervision, 114
Staff of hospital, volunteer relation to,
7-9, 17, 32-34, 56-57, 150-153
Student volunteers, *See* College; High
School
Supervision of volunteers
as agency investment, 17
attitudes affected by, 114-115
career choice related to, 115-116
effectiveness increased by, 8-9, 113-116
emotional support by, 40-41, 117
follow-up study of effects of, 111-119
length of service affected by, 114
See also Orientation; Training
Supervisor of patients in workshops, 68-
69, 74
Supervisor of volunteers
assessment by student volunteers, 117-
118
occupational therapist as, 61, 63
psychiatrist as, 130, 131-132
psychologist as, 95-96
qualifications for case aide program,
42
social worker as, 36, 41-42, 46-48,
130-131
tasks of, as shown by study, 116-117
training for case aide program, 42
ward staff as, 57, 59
See also Coordinator
Supervisory procedures
of case aides, 36, 38, 40-42, 46, 47-
48, 50
of clinic volunteers, 17
of college students, 111-119
of high school students, 124-125, 131-
132
of social club volunteers, **92-93**
of social aides, 101

of VISTA volunteers, 56-57

T

Therapeutic involvement (training of
volunteers), 8, 9
Torchlighters (social club), 95, 98
See also Center Club
Training of case aide supervisors, 42
Training of volunteers
advanced case aide training, 43-44
focus of, for hospital volunteers, 30
in Commonwealth Service Corps, 21
in VISTA, 54, 56-57
therapeutic involvement as, 8-9
See also Orientation; Supervision
Transporation
of high school volunteers, 123, 127,
128
of outpatients, 11
of social club members, 98
Team approach
of case aides, 43
of college careers program, 142

U

Unit system in mental hospitals, 26-27
effect on volunteer programs, 30

V

Veterans Administration Hospital youth
volunteer program, 120-128
VISTA volunteer program, 52-59
Volunteers, *See subheadings*

W

Wages in paid workshop, 67, 71
Waiting room assistants, 14
Workshop, sheltered, 65-72, 73-76

Y

Youth volunteer program, *See* College;
High school